It's another Quality Book from CGP

This book is for 8-9 year olds.

It contains lots of tricky questions designed to
make you sweat — because that's the only
way you'll get any better.

It's also got some daft bits in to try and make
the whole experience at least vaguely
entertaining for you.

What CGP is all about

Our sole aim here at CGP is to produce the highest quality
books — carefully written, immaculately presented and
dangerously close to being funny.

Then we work our socks off to get them out to you
— at the cheapest possible prices.

Contents

Published by CGP

Contributors:
Simon Cook
Taissa Csáky
Gemma Hallam
Simon Little
Iain Nash
Andy Park
Glenn Rogers

ISBN: 978 1 84146 158 8

Groovy website: www.cgpbooks.co.uk
Jolly bits of clipart from CorelDRAW®
Printed by Elanders Ltd, Newcastle upon Tyne.

Based on the classic CGP style created by Richard Parsons.

Alphabetical Order

When you put words in **alphabetical order**, look at the first letter of each word.
If they're the same, you'll have to look at the second, third or fourth letters instead.

cat goes before *dog*   *catastrophe* goes before *catch*

Q1 Put these names in alphabetical order using their first and second letters.

Corey, Billy, Kerry, Molly → *Billy, Corey, Kerry, Molly*

Peter, Gareth, Lucy, Fred, Michelle → *Fred Gareth Lucy Michelle Peter*

Jayne, Jenny, Becky, Anil, David → *Anil Becky David Jayne Jenny*

Han, Chewie, Luke, Leia, Obi-Wan → *Chewie Han Leia Luke Obi-Wan*

Q2 Put these words in alphabetical order.
Don't forget to look at the third and fourth letters if you need to.

cabbage, chance, church, cave, chap, coffee

cabbage, cave, chance, chap, church, coffee

lamb, lady, llama, lamp, lava, later

lady lamb lamp later lava llama

apartment, apatosaurus, antifreeze, ant, anorak, apple

....

Q3 Put these names in alphabetical order.

Bruce, Brian, Brunhilda, Brenda

....

Jayne, Jasmine, Jaswinder, Zorg, Janet

....

Mike, Miroslav, Michelle, Michael, Mina

....

English Workbook — Year 4

Verbs

Verbs tell you what's happening in the **past**, the **present** or the **future**.

Past

He ate toads.   He was eating toads.

Q1 Circle the verbs that are in the **past tense**.

Where are the caravans?

Over there, past tents.

(went)   go   find   found

have   had   gave   give

is staying   stayed   slept   was sleeping

Present

He eats toads.   He is eating toads.

Q2 Change these sentences so that the verbs are in the **present tense**.

I was having a few computer problems.

I am having a few computer problems.

It was very sunny.

....

Jane had a letter to post.

....

Future   *I will eat toads*

Q3 Change these sentences so that they're in the **future tense**.

I try to finish my book.   *We sing Christmas carols.*

I will try to finish my book.   ....

Harry went to Nottingham.   *It is raining.*

....

Verbs

The different forms of verbs are called **tenses**. Stories and reports are in the **past tense**. Instructions and explanations are in the **present**. Forecasts are in the **future tense**.

Q4 Read Lauren's report on how she did a science experiment. Change the verbs to the present tense to turn it into instructions. The first line is done for you.

I wrapped one ice cube in paper, one in foil and one in cheesecake. I left them on a plate. I looked at them every 2 minutes and wrote down the time when each one melted. Then I compared the results.

Wrap one ice cube in paper, one in foil and one in cheesecake.

Q5 Look at this weather forecast. Imagine it was exactly right. Write a weather diary for the day, changing the verbs from future to past tense.

Today will start off bright and sunny. There will be some ground frost, which will melt by mid-morning. There will be a cold wind from the West, bringing in some cloud. It will rain chocolate drops in the afternoon. Temperatures will be between 5 and 10 degrees Celsius.

Today started off bright and sunny. There was...

Double Letters

Some words have **double letters** in the middle, like 'butter' and 'kettle'. You can't tell they're there when you say the word.

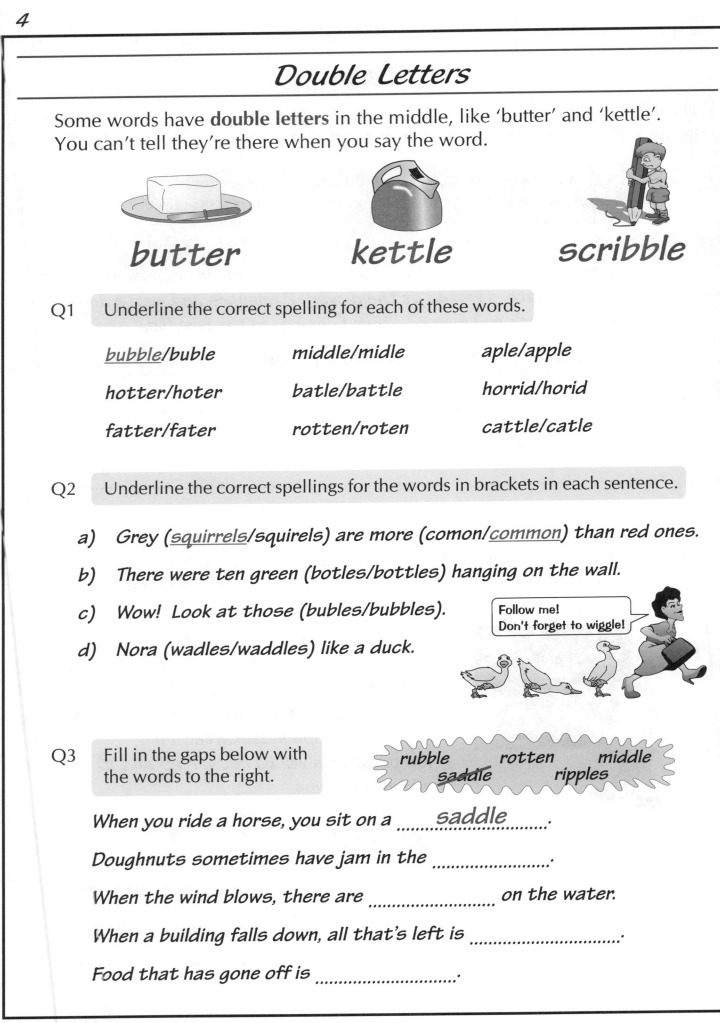

butter   kettle   scribble

Q1   Underline the correct spelling for each of these words.

bubble/buble   middle/midle   aple/apple

hotter/hoter   batle/battle   horrid/horid

fatter/fater   rotten/roten   cattle/catle

Q2   Underline the correct spellings for the words in brackets in each sentence.

a)   Grey (squirrels/squirels) are more (comon/common) than red ones.

b)   There were ten green (botles/bottles) hanging on the wall.

c)   Wow! Look at those (bubles/bubbles).

d)   Nora (wadles/waddles) like a duck.

Follow me!
Don't forget to wiggle!

Q3   Fill in the gaps below with the words to the right.

rubble   rotten   middle
saddle   ripples

When you ride a horse, you sit on a ....saddle........... .

Doughnuts sometimes have jam in the ....

When the wind blows, there are .... on the water.

When a building falls down, all that's left is ....

Food that has gone off is ....

Homophones

Homophones are different words that sound the same.

two   *too*   *to*

To is for going **to** a place, or it is part of a verb. **Two** means the number **2**.
Too means 'also' or '**too** much/little'.

Q1   Put a circle around the right word to complete each sentence.

a)   Ow! This soup's (to/**too**) hot.

b)   I've got (two/to) pet rabbits.

c)   I can't go in. That ghost is (to/too) scary.

d)   Can we go (to/too) the cinema instead?

Q2   **Piece** means 'a little bit'. **Peace** means 'quiet 'or the opposite of war.
Put a circle around the correct words.

a)   Can I have another (**piece**/peace) of cake?

b)   Can I have some (piece/peace) and quiet?

c)   The plate broke into a thousand (peaces/pieces).

d)   "(Peaces/Pieces) of eight!" squawked the parrot.

Q3   **There** means 'that place'. **They're** is short for 'they are'.
Their means 'belonging to them'. Put a circle around the correct words.

a)   Look at my gerbils, (**they're**/their) so cute!

b)   (There/their) is a party tonight at Susan's house.

c)   Sam and Ernie have lost (there/their) coats.

d)   It's alright, (they're/their) over (there/they're).

e)   Check out the carrots, (there/they're) dancing!

Regular and Irregular Verbs

Most verbs have the same pattern of endings.
You add different endings to form the **past**, **present** and **future** tenses.

He paints.
He is painting.

= **present tense**

He painted
the bench.

= **past tense**

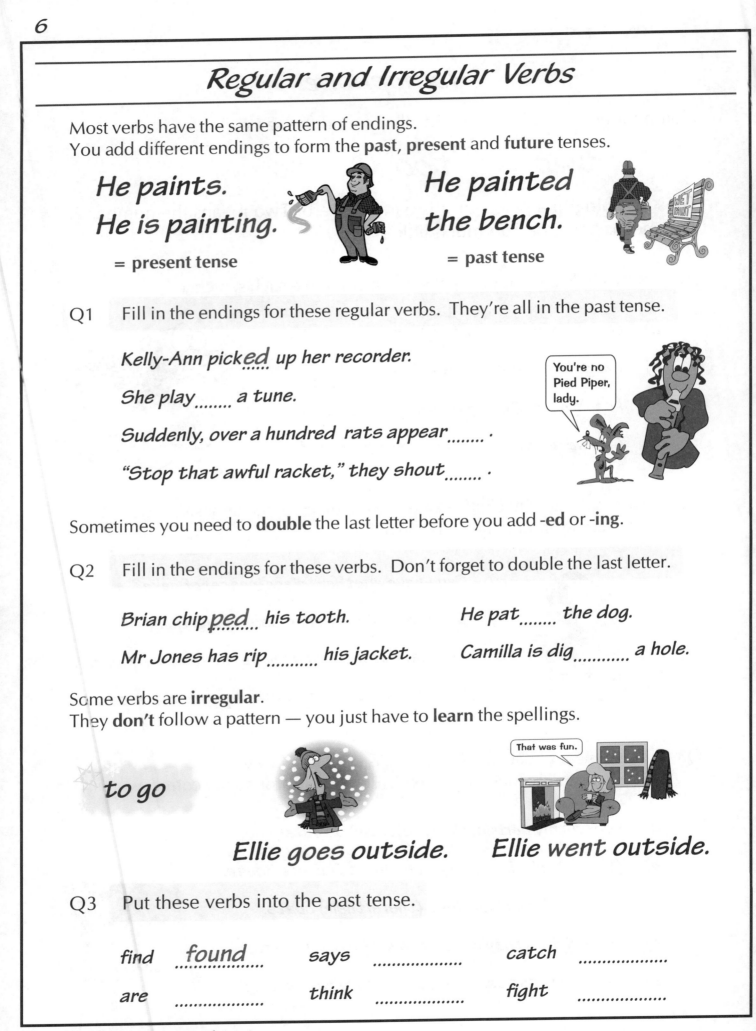

Q1   Fill in the endings for these regular verbs. They're all in the past tense.

Kelly-Ann pick_ed_ up her recorder.

She play........ a tune.

Suddenly, over a hundred rats appear........ .

"Stop that awful racket," they shout........ .

You're no Pied Piper, lady.

Sometimes you need to **double** the last letter before you add **-ed** or **-ing**.

Q2   Fill in the endings for these verbs. Don't forget to double the last letter.

Brian chip_ped_ his tooth.

Mr Jones has rip.......... his jacket.

He pat........ the dog.

Camilla is dig........... a hole.

Some verbs are **irregular**.
They **don't** follow a pattern — you just have to **learn** the spellings.

to go

That was fun.

Ellie goes outside.

Ellie went outside.

Q3   Put these verbs into the past tense.

find	_found_	says	....	catch	....
are	....	think	....	fight	....

Regular and Irregular Verbs

Q4 Change these sentences so that they're in the past tense.

I catch the bus at half past eight.

I caught the bus at half past eight.

Sally can't come to the party.

....

Terry buys oranges.

....

Roland rings his mates on his mobile phone.

....

Buy oranges! Sell grapefruit!

Q5 Look at this piece about a bad day. The verbs are missing. Finish the story using the correct verbs from the list.

ran   jumped   realised   ~~woke up~~   was sleeping   asked   looked   staggered   was   laughed

I _woke up_ late this morning. One minute I

........................, and the next I .... at the clock

and it .... nine o'clock already. I .... out

of bed and .... all the way to school.

When I .... into the classroom, everyone

.... at me.

"What do you think you're wearing?" .... the

teacher angrily.

I suddenly .... I was still in my pyjamas.

8

Suffixes

Suffixes are groups of letters added to the end of a word.
They change the meaning of the word and what it's used for in a sentence.

It grew dark.   dark + ness   Darkness fell.

Here's the suffix.   This is the new word.

Q1 Look at the list of words with suffixes below.
Match up all the words with the same suffix.

childhood   friendship   amazement
sadness   excitement   leadership
adulthood   companionship   amusement
happiness   parenthood   illness

Are you alright up there, Mr Darkness?

-ness	-hood	-ship	-ment
happiness	....	leadership	....
....	....	....	....
....	....	....	....

Q2 Do these word sums to make some common words with suffixes.
These words have the suffixes **-al**, **-ary** or **-ic**.

origin   +   al   =   original   realist   +   ic   = ...

custom +   ary = ...   music   +   al   = ...

person +   al   = ...

diet   +   ary = ...

artist   +   ic   = ...

caution +   ary = ...

Suffixes

Suffixes

Q3 Complete each word sum with the correct suffix to make a new word.

neighbour + hood/ness = ...neighbourhood...

kind + ness/ship = ...

member + ness/ship = ...

fair + hood/ness = ...

partner + ship/ness = ...

knight + ness/hood = ...

premier + hood/ship = ...

When you add a suffix, some words lose a letter from their end.

imagine + ary = imaginary

Take off the letter -**e**.   There's no -**e** in 'imaginary'.

Some words change their final letter from -**y** to -**i** when they add a suffix.

happy + ness = happiness

Take off the final -**y**.   Put -**i** instead and add the suffix.

Q4 Add each word to the suffix to make a new word.
Remember to take off any extra -**e**'s, and change any -**y**'s to -**i**'s.

majesty + ic = ...majestic...

argue + ment = ...

likely + hood = ...

lazy + ness = ...

Don't forget
to make the
changes.

Phonemes

Phonemes are the smallest unit of sound in a word.
A phoneme can be one letter or more, but it's always only **one sound**.

beat   house   cook

These are all **phonemes**.

Q1 Look at the **red** phonemes in each of these lists of words.
Circle the odd word out in each list.

Which ones sound different?

a) hope, slope, rope, (slip)

b) cat, sit, mat, rat

c) blow, crow, flaw, slow

d) pig, dig, wig, jug

e) plod, rid, rod, cod

Q2 Choose the correct phoneme to finish each word.

grow	(oa) (ow)	f......d	(ei) (oo)
f......sh	(au) (i)	h......!	(ou) (ow)
br......d	(ea) (oi)	p.....ll	(u) (aw)
cl......	(ou) (aw)	holid.....	(aw) (ay)

Q3 Give two more words using each of the phonemes in **red**.

care	......spare......	......rare......
fly	....	....
lip	....	....
hair	....	....
star	....	....

Think hard.

Rhymes

Two words rhyme when their endings sound the same.

dog rhymes with **frog**   **tree** rhymes with **me**

Rhyming words don't have to be spelt the same way. They just sound the same.

Q1   Match up each word on the left with the one it rhymes with on the right.

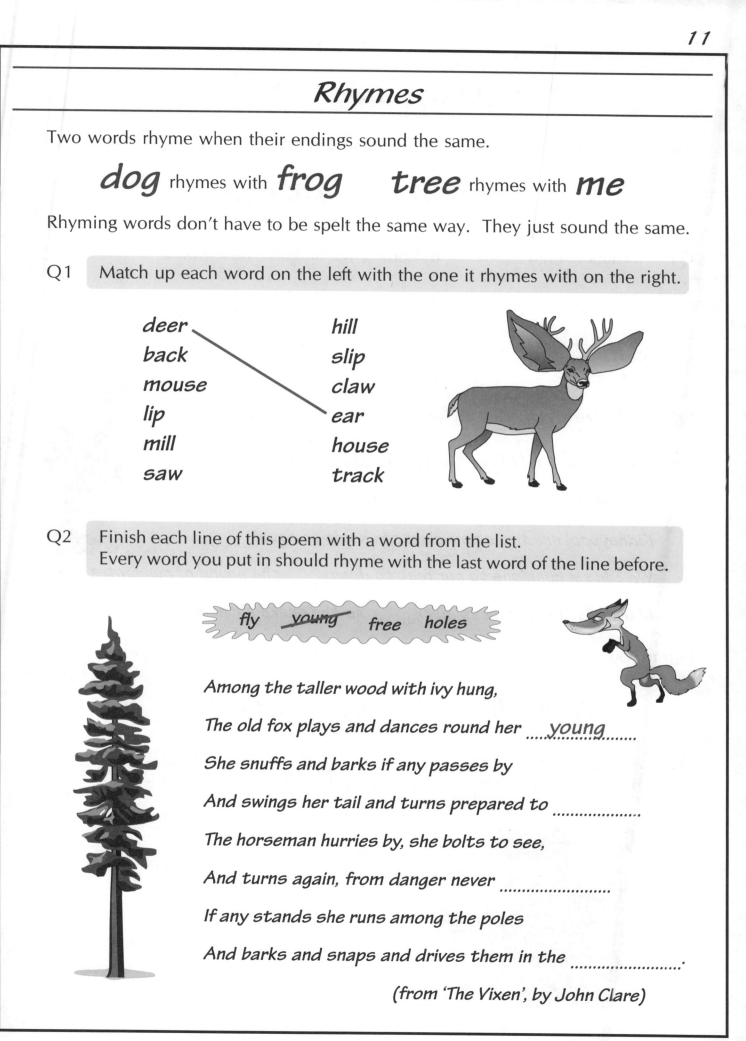

deer   hill
back   slip
mouse   claw
lip   ear
mill   house
saw   track

Q2   Finish each line of this poem with a word from the list.
Every word you put in should rhyme with the last word of the line before.

fly   ~~young~~   free   holes

Among the taller wood with ivy hung,

The old fox plays and dances round her ....young.......

She snuffs and barks if any passes by

And swings her tail and turns prepared to ....

The horseman hurries by, she bolts to see,

And turns again, from danger never ....

If any stands she runs among the poles

And barks and snaps and drives them in the ....

(from 'The Vixen', by John Clare)

Making Verbs from Other Words

Many words can be made into **verbs** by adding **extra letters** to the end of the word.

equalize   stiffen

Q1 Write out the verbs made by adding -**ize** or -**en** to these words.

familiar + ize _familiarize_   short + en ....

thick + en ....   final + ize ....

Q2 Add -**ize** or -**en** to the unfinished verbs in these sentences.

I'm going to liquid _ize_ these bananas and make milk shake.

You can strength .... the joints with glue.

Kidneypool need to score eighteen goals to equal ....

We can tie cushions to our feet to dead .... the sound of our footsteps.

Mark felt his heartbeat quick .... as the snake slithered closer.

Before you add -**en** to a word you sometimes have to double the last letter.

sad + en ➡ sadden

Q3 Add -**en** to these words.
Be careful — you don't need to double the last letter for all of them.

DOUBLE D SALOON

ENTRY
FORBIDDEN
TO STRANGERS

mad + en _madden_

thick + en ....

hard + en ....

soft + en ....

forbid + en ....

glad + en ....

Making Verbs from Other Words

Another ending you can add on to words to make verbs is **-ify**.

solid + ify ➡ solidify

-ify means **make**, so **solidify** means **make solid**.

When you add **-ify** you often have to take away letters from the original word.

simple + ify ➡ simplify

Take away the **e** first.

Q4 Draw lines to show which words the **-ify** words are based on.

falsify   terror

beautify   code

terrify   horror

codify   false

horrify   beauty

uglify   ugly

Q5 The endings on these words have been swapped around by mistake. Write them out with the proper endings.

widize

....*widen*....

soliden

....

personalify

....

sadize

....

equalify

....

justen

....

Adverbs

Adverbs give more detail about something else in the sentence.

Warren ate the carrots noisily. ← Lots of adverbs end with **-ly**.

The adverb tells you more about how Warren **ate** the carrots.

Q1   Put a ring round all the adverbs in this story. There are ten altogether.

Natasha looked (carefully) through the glass door. The other children were watching a video and the room was lit dimly. The teacher was nowhere to be seen, so Natasha slowly opened the door. Nobody noticed her as she crept stealthily across the back of the room. Her heart was beating wildly, but her feet moved soundlessly over the floor.

Natasha seemed to have reached her desk safely, but suddenly the lights clicked on. The teacher looked down angrily at Natasha and growled, "This really has to stop."

Q2   Choose the best adverb to finish off these sentences.

The baby yawned _sleepily_ . (sleepily/fiercely)

House cats are _____ related to tigers. (closely/slowly)

Rivers flow more _____ after heavy rain. (kindly/swiftly)

The fishermen sang _____ all the way home. (foggily/cheerfully)

The chocolate sauce smelt _____ of garlic. (swiftly/faintly)

The ballerinas danced _____ across the stage. (grumpily/gracefully)

Adverbs

Q3 Adverbs always describe another word in the sentence.
Which words do the adverbs in these sentences describe?

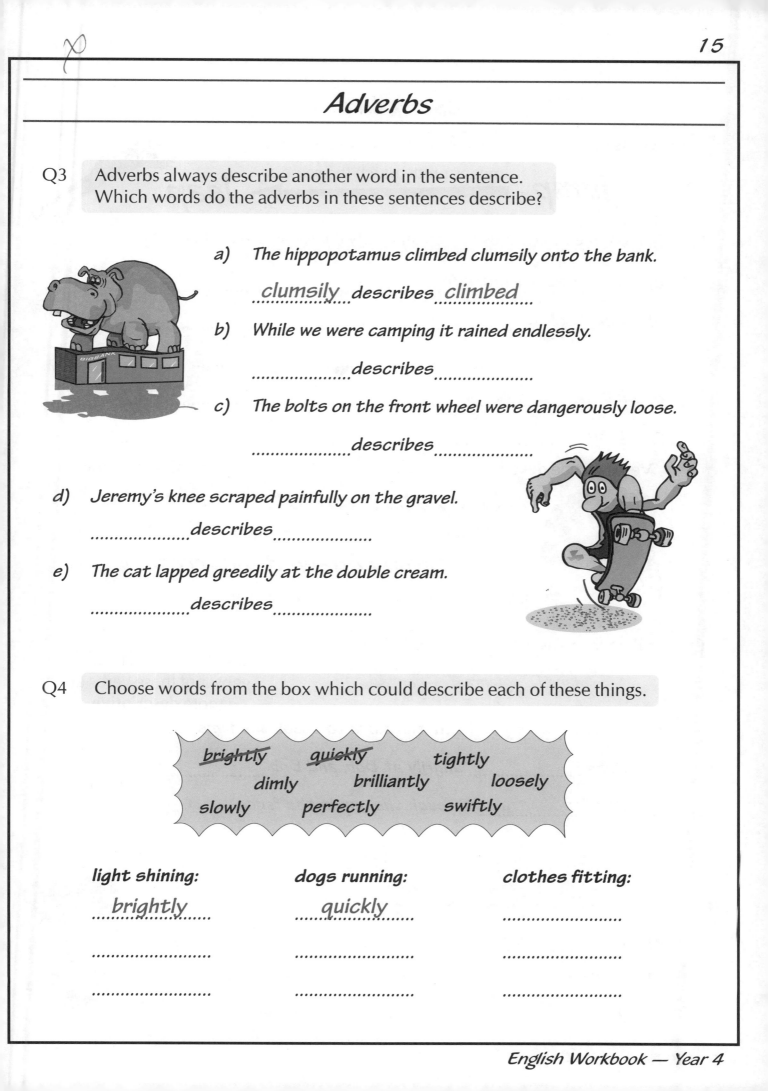

a)   The hippopotamus climbed clumsily onto the bank.

.....*clumsily*..... describes .....*climbed*.....

b)   While we were camping it rained endlessly.

.....................describes.....................

c)   The bolts on the front wheel were dangerously loose.

.....................describes.....................

d)   Jeremy's knee scraped painfully on the gravel.

.....................describes.....................

e)   The cat lapped greedily at the double cream.

.....................describes.....................

Q4   Choose words from the box which could describe each of these things.

> ~~*brightly*~~   ~~*quickly*~~   *tightly*
>   *dimly*   *brilliantly*   *loosely*
>   *slowly*   *perfectly*   *swiftly*

light shining: **dogs running:**   **clothes fitting:**

.....*brightly*.....   .....*quickly*.....   ....

....

....

16

Descriptive Verbs

Some **verbs** mean almost the same thing as another verb.

jump   means pretty much the same as   leap

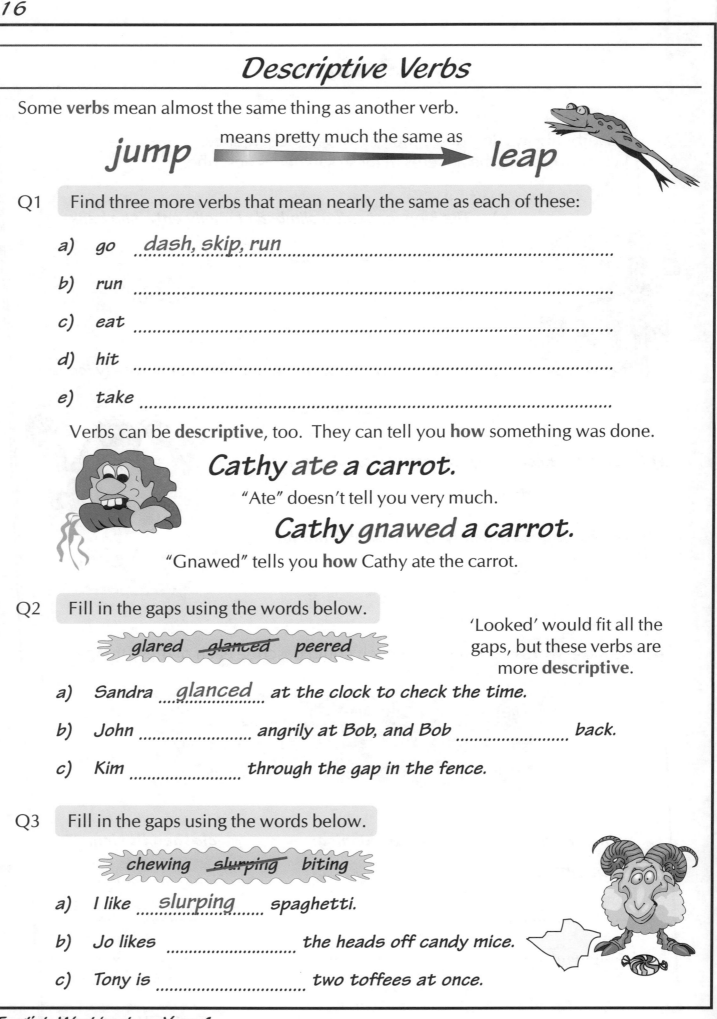

Q1 Find three more verbs that mean nearly the same as each of these:

a) go   _dash, skip, run_ ....

b) run ....

c) eat ....

d) hit ....

e) take ....

Verbs can be **descriptive**, too. They can tell you **how** something was done.

Cathy ate a carrot.

"Ate" doesn't tell you very much.

Cathy gnawed a carrot.

"Gnawed" tells you **how** Cathy ate the carrot.

Q2 Fill in the gaps using the words below.

glared   ~~glanced~~   peered

'Looked' would fit all the gaps, but these verbs are more **descriptive**.

a) Sandra __glanced__ at the clock to check the time.

b) John .... angrily at Bob, and Bob .... back.

c) Kim .... through the gap in the fence.

Q3 Fill in the gaps using the words below.

chewing   ~~slurping~~   biting

a) I like __slurping__ spaghetti.

b) Jo likes .... the heads off candy mice.

c) Tony is .... two toffees at once.

English Workbook — Year 4

Descriptive Verbs

Q4 Fill in the gaps with words from the box.

limped   pinched   ran   dashed
sped   ~~grabbed~~   hurled

a) Neil _grabbed_ the book out of my hand.

b) Kevin _____ out of the house and _____
as fast as he could to the bus stop.

c) Becky _____ the welly as far as she could.

d) Karen _____ because her foot hurt.

e) Someone's _____ my best pencil!

f) A police car _____ past with its lights flashing.

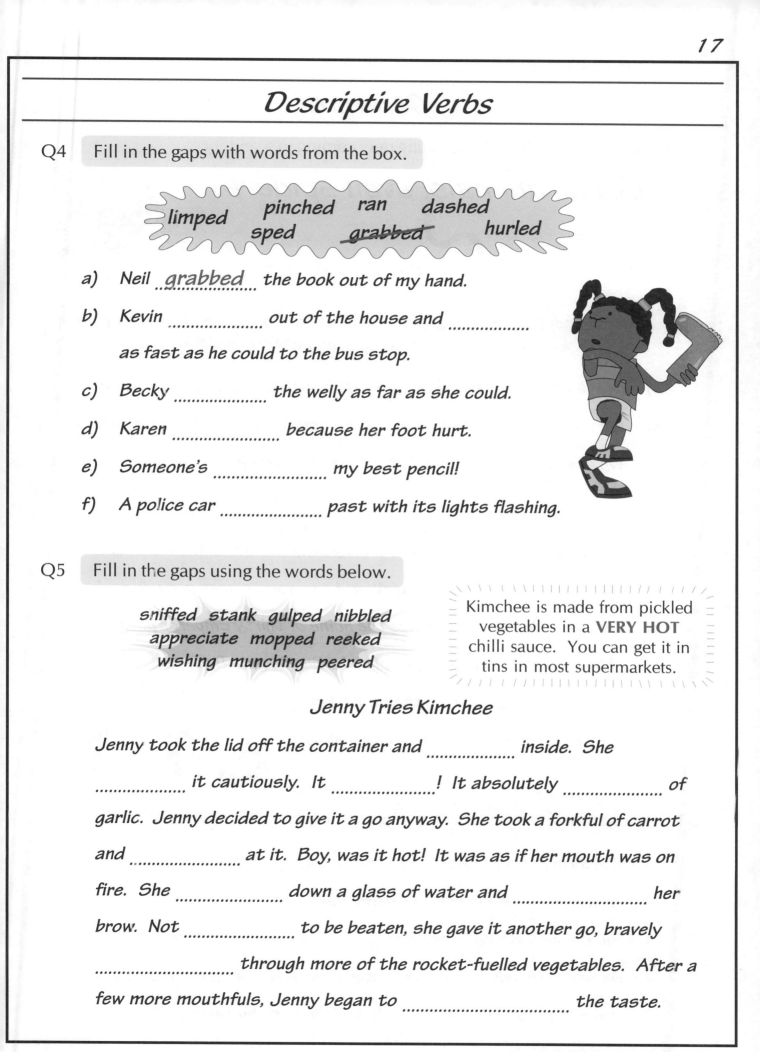

Q5 Fill in the gaps using the words below.

sniffed   stank   gulped   nibbled
appreciate   mopped   reeked
wishing   munching   peered

Kimchee is made from pickled vegetables in a **VERY HOT** chilli sauce. You can get it in tins in most supermarkets.

Jenny Tries Kimchee

Jenny took the lid off the container and _____ inside. She
_____ it cautiously. It _____! It absolutely _____ of
garlic. Jenny decided to give it a go anyway. She took a forkful of carrot
and _____ at it. Boy, was it hot! It was as if her mouth was on
fire. She _____ down a glass of water and _____ her
brow. Not _____ to be beaten, she gave it another go, bravely
_____ through more of the rocket-fuelled vegetables. After a
few more mouthfuls, Jenny began to _____ the taste.

18

Commas

Commas show that there's something new coming in a sentence.

I like all animals, even spiders.

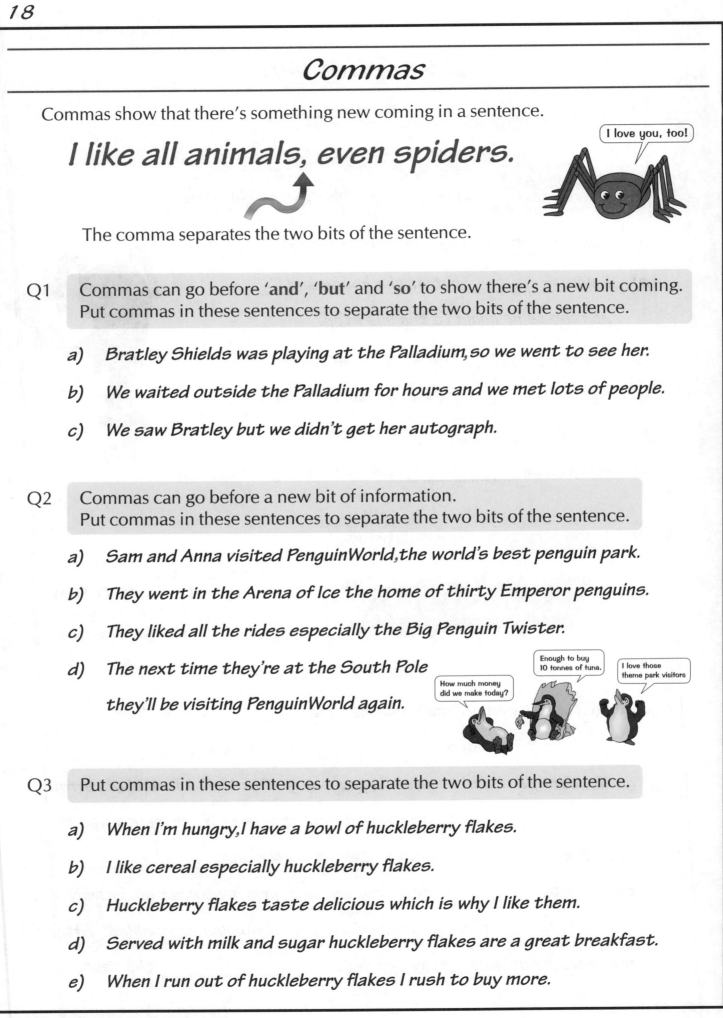

I love you, too!

The comma separates the two bits of the sentence.

Q1 Commas can go before 'and', 'but' and 'so' to show there's a new bit coming.
Put commas in these sentences to separate the two bits of the sentence.

a) Bratley Shields was playing at the Palladium, so we went to see her.

b) We waited outside the Palladium for hours and we met lots of people.

c) We saw Bratley but we didn't get her autograph.

Q2 Commas can go before a new bit of information.
Put commas in these sentences to separate the two bits of the sentence.

a) Sam and Anna visited PenguinWorld, the world's best penguin park.

b) They went in the Arena of Ice the home of thirty Emperor penguins.

c) They liked all the rides especially the Big Penguin Twister.

d) The next time they're at the South Pole
they'll be visiting PenguinWorld again.

How much money did we make today?

Enough to buy 10 tonnes of tuna.

I love those theme park visitors

Q3 Put commas in these sentences to separate the two bits of the sentence.

a) When I'm hungry, I have a bowl of huckleberry flakes.

b) I like cereal especially huckleberry flakes.

c) Huckleberry flakes taste delicious which is why I like them.

d) Served with milk and sugar huckleberry flakes are a great breakfast.

e) When I run out of huckleberry flakes I rush to buy more.

English Workbook — Year 4

Commas

Commas are also used like brackets to separate off bits of the sentence.

The Mayor, Mrs Moss, will judge the Amusing Marrow contest.

You could take these words out and the sentence would still make sense.

So, this marrow walks into a bar...

The Mayor will judge the Amusing Marrow contest.

Q4 Put commas in the right places in these sentences.

a) *Dr Brookes and Mrs Johnson, the receptionist, are doing a sponsored run.*

b) *Billy who'd never played Frogball before won the prize.*

c) *Barbara Brolly the weather forecaster is opening the new supermarket.*

d) *I saw Dave whose grandad invented flavoured crisps eating plain crisps.*

e) *Flavoured crisps as Dave's grandad used to say are the best.*

Q5 Put commas in the right places in this passage.

Next week I'm going to Canada to see my aunt and uncle. It's a long flight about 8 hours so I'll be really tired. When I get there I'll probably go straight to bed.

My uncle who's a fireman is going to show me around. I'm looking forward to seeing all the sights especially Niagara Falls. Hopefully he'll take me to an ice hockey game which is something I've never done before. I'm going to take loads of photos just so you can see what my trip to Canada was like .

Dad, don't do that! Aaarrrgghh.

Tee hee!

A spectacular waterfall.

Syllables

All words are made of **syllables**.
Syllables are the bits you say separately, a bit like the **beats** in music.

ma-gic
There are **two** syllables in magic...

e-le-phant
...but **three** in elephant.

a, e, i, o and **u** are **vowels** — and sometimes **y**. All other letters are **consonants**.

Every syllable has at least one **vowel**.

Q1 Join these syllables to make words.

doc + tor ....*doctor*....   gi + raffe ....

thou + sand ....   pi + a + no ....

hap + pi + ness .... sil + ly ....

Q2 Circle the number of syllables in each of these words.

dog   (1) 2 3 4   elbow   1 2 3 4

carpet 1 2 3 4   rhinoceros 1 2 3 4

paper   1 2 3 4   furniture 1 2 3 4

To break a word into syllables, say it slowly out loud.
Each separate sound is a syllable.

calendar ➡ cal + en + dar
              ca + lend + ar

There is often **more than one way** to split a word into syllables.

Q3 Split each of these words up into syllables.

record ➡ ....*rec*.... + ...*ord*....

shadow ➡ .... + ...

confusing ➡ .... + ... + ...

messages ➡ .... + ... + ...

Did someone say, "silly bull"?

'i' Before 'e' and 'e' Before 'i'

When you get the letters **i** and **e** together, the **i** usually goes **before** the **e**.

field   chief   shield   friend

Q1   Circle the right spelling of each word.

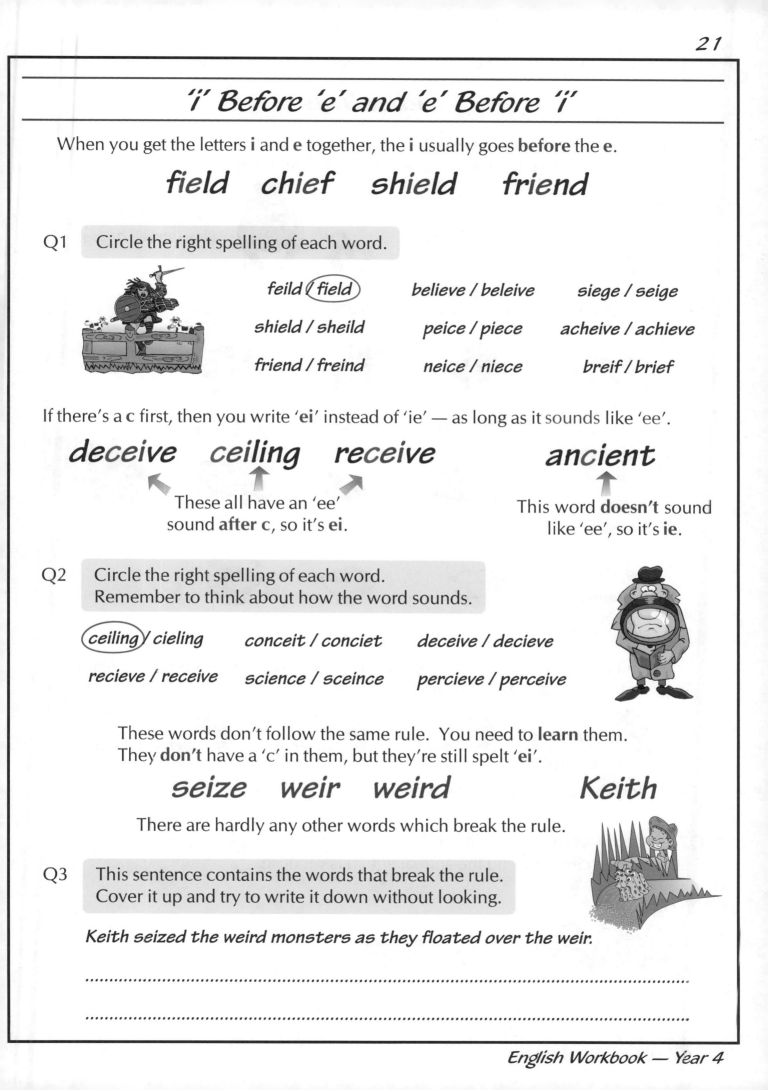

feild / (field)   believe / beleive   siege / seige

shield / sheild   peice / piece   acheive / achieve

friend / freind   neice / niece   breif / brief

If there's a **c** first, then you write '**ei**' instead of '**ie**' — as long as it sounds like 'ee'.

de**ce**ive   **ce**iling   re**ce**ive   an**ci**ent

These all have an 'ee' sound **after c**, so it's **ei**.

This word **doesn't** sound like 'ee', so it's **ie**.

Q2   Circle the right spelling of each word.
Remember to think about how the word sounds.

(ceiling) / cieling   conceit / conciet   deceive / decieve

recieve / receive   science / sceince   percieve / perceive

These words don't follow the same rule. You need to **learn** them.
They **don't** have a 'c' in them, but they're still spelt '**ei**'.

seize   weir   weird   Keith

There are hardly any other words which break the rule.

Q3   This sentence contains the words that break the rule.
Cover it up and try to write it down without looking.

Keith seized the weird monsters as they floated over the weir.

....

....

Adjectives

Adjectives are words used to **describe** things.
You can use adjectives to describe one thing in different ways.

A bath can be cold, warm, hot, or boiling.

A dog can be tiny, small, or big.

Q1 Match the words on the left with with the pictures.

ancient
youthful
old

enormous
big
tiny
small

good
fantastic
okay

..youthful..   ...old...   ..ancient..

....

....

You don't have to use a different word every time you want to describe something.
You can use **very**, **quite** or **extremely** with the same word.

quite long
or longish

long

very long

extremely long

Longish means long, but not very long.

Q2 Put the words **very**, **quite** and **extremely** in the right places below.
Draw a circle around the animal which is **smallish**.

.... *small*

.... *small*   *small*   .... *small*

Adjectives

You can give a word a **stronger** meaning by adding **-er** and **-est**.

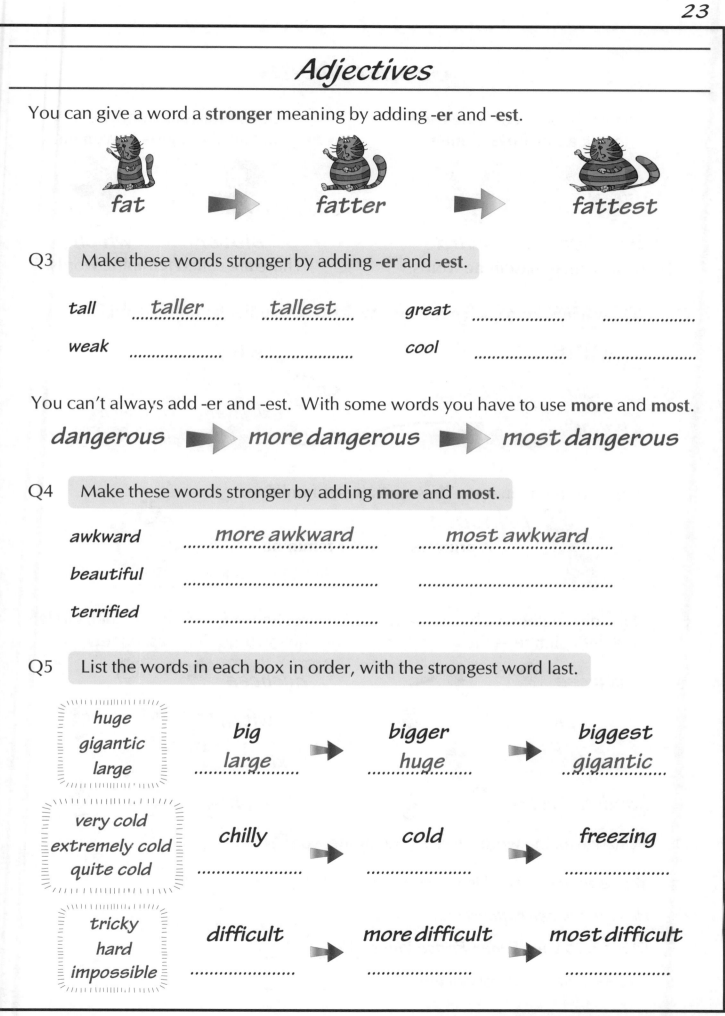

fat ➤ fatter ➤ fattest

Q3 Make these words stronger by adding **-er** and **-est**.

tall _taller_ _tallest_ great ....

weak .... cool ....

You can't always add -er and -est. With some words you have to use **more** and **most**.

dangerous ➤ *more dangerous* ➤ *most dangerous*

Q4 Make these words stronger by adding **more** and **most**.

awkward _more awkward_ _most awkward_

beautiful ....

terrified ....

Q5 List the words in each box in order, with the strongest word last.

huge
gigantic
large

big
large ➤ bigger
huge ➤ biggest
gigantic

very cold
extremely cold
quite cold

chilly
.... ➤ cold
.... ➤ freezing
....

tricky
hard
impossible

difficult
.... ➤ more difficult
.... ➤ most difficult
....

Gender Words

Some words can only be used to talk about **boys** or **men**.

brother   **wizard**

These are called **masculine** words.

Other words can only be used to talk about **girls** or **women**.

sister   **witch**

These are called **feminine** words.

Q1 Draw a line from each masculine word to the similar feminine word.

masculine

king   fox
uncle
brother   boy
son

feminine

sister   vixen
daughter   queen
girl   aunt

Some words end in **-ess**. These are always **feminine**.

princess

A **princess** is always **feminine**.

That's just so true.

Q2 Decide whether each of these words is masculine or feminine and then circle the right picture — the girl if it's feminine and the boy if it's masculine.

tigress

sir

uncle

headmistress

duchess

witch

king

nephew

Q3 Change all the words in red to feminine words.

Your son has eaten his pencil case.   daughter   her

He can see her nephew from there.   ....

Don't hurt your finger, Prince Vince.   ....

Please, can I have my bull back?   ....

Old Words

Words come into fashion and then go out again. They're just like hairstyles or clothes. Some words that were used all the time in the past sound really old-fashioned now.

Q1 Draw lines to match pictures to the old words.

frock
Mrs Welly's new frock looks lovely. It's got loads of pretty flowers on the front and the sleeves.

wireless
Turn on the wireless — the news is coming on.

wigging
If Mr. Simpson catches us cheating in the exam, he'll give us a good wigging.

flying machine
The flying machine completed the journey from London to Delhi in only six days.

Q2 Write down a more up-to-date version of each of the words in **red** below.

"Turn on the wireless, Jonesy." ....radio..........

"You turn it on. I haven't finished eating my grub yet." ....

"Come on — there's a programme on at seven that's absolutely ripping, and I don't want to miss it." ....

"Oh, I know. About the chap who said he'd rowed across the Atlantic in a bathtub. I don't believe anybody could do that — it all sounds like a lot of humbug to me." ....

"I'm sure it's true. In fact, I'll wager you a pound that it is." ....

Definitions

A definition tells you **what a word means**.

microchip ➡ *one of the tiny pieces in a computer that make it work*

This is the **definition** — it explains what a microchip is, but in **easy words**.

Dictionaries are a good place to find definitions.

Q1 Draw a line from each word to its definition.

windmill

microwave oven

comedian

an electronic oven that cooks food very quickly

someone who entertains people by making them laugh

a kind of factory that uses wind to make the machinery work

Q2 The definitions of these words are all mixed up. Write the definitions out properly below.

a musical instrument, with four legs, for moving over smooth ground

a shoe, with strings, kept as a pet

a small furry animal, with wheels, played with the fingers

cat   *a small furry animal, with four legs, kept as a pet*

roller skate   ....

guitar   ....

Q3 Write a short definition for each of these words.

car   *a machine for carrying small numbers of people*

knife   ....

fork   ....

pencil   ....

Definitions

There are lots of things you **could** say about scissors —

scissors   *a cutting tool with two sharp blades, for cutting cloth, paper or fingernails, sometimes with plastic handles*

To give a **good definition** you only need to say the most important things.

scissors   *a cutting tool with two sharp blades*

Q4   Circle the four most important words in these definitions.

wardrobe   *a* (large) (bedroom) (cupboard), *used for storing* (clothes)

plum   *a soft, juicy fruit with a stone*

parrot   *a noisy, colourful bird found in tropical regions*

Q5   For this question you need to write the shortest possible definitions. Use the best four words, then the best three, two, and one.

wardrobe   4 words: *large bedroom clothes cupboard*

                3 words: *large clothes cupboard*

                2 words: *clothes cupboard*

                1 word: *cupboard*

plum   4 words: ....

            3 words: ....

            2 words: ....

            1 word: ....

parrot   4 words: ....

            3 words: ....

            2 words: ....

            1 word: ....

Forming Adjectives

Some **nouns** and **verbs** can be changed into **adjectives**, by simply adding a **suffix**.

Here the verb '**wash**' is the starting word.

wash + '-able'

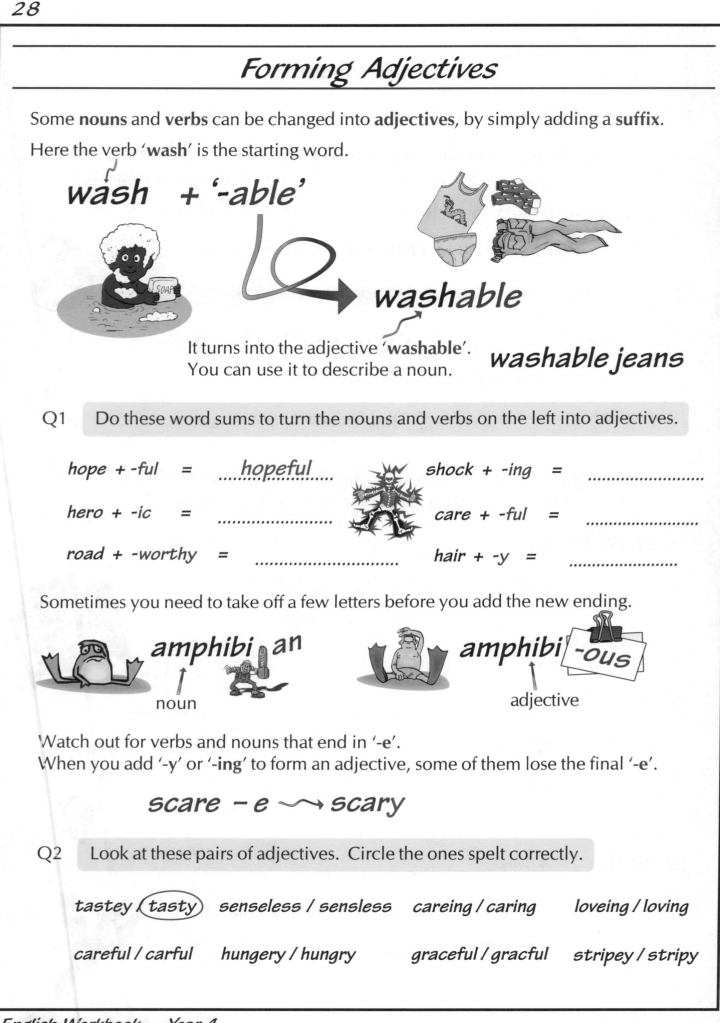

washable

It turns into the adjective '**washable**'.
You can use it to describe a noun.

washable jeans

Q1   Do these word sums to turn the nouns and verbs on the left into adjectives.

hope + -ful   = ...hopeful...........

hero + -ic   = ...

road + -worthy   = ...

shock + -ing   = ...

care + -ful   = ...

hair + -y   = ...

Sometimes you need to take off a few letters before you add the new ending.

amphibi an

noun

amphibi -ous

adjective

Watch out for verbs and nouns that end in '**-e**'.
When you add '**-y**' or '**-ing**' to form an adjective, some of them lose the final '**-e**'.

scare – e ⤳ scary

Q2   Look at these pairs of adjectives. Circle the ones spelt correctly.

tastey (tasty)   senseless / sensless   careing / caring   loveing / loving

careful / carful   hungery / hungry   graceful / gracful   stripey / stripy

Forming Adjectives

Q3 | Add the right ending to each word to turn it into an adjective.

broke ...... *broken* ......

electric ....

care ....

spin ....

-ning

-n   -less

-al

Q4 | Add the right ending to turn each of these nouns into adjectives. You might have to take letters off to give the right spelling.

-ic   -ous

acid ...... *acidic* ......   villain ....

danger ....   rhythm ....

ridicule ....   economy ....

mountain ....   melody ....

Lots of words ending in '-**ing**' can be used as adjectives as well as verbs.

a charming man   a laughing policewoman

Q5 | Look at the sentences below. Write each one out again. Turn the words in brackets into adjectives by adding '-**ing**'.

The (sing) frog loved to play the piano.

The singing frog loved to play the piano.

Some words lose the final '-**e**' before adding '-**ing**.'

The (dare) climber was stuck in a (frighten) position.

....

Lucy followed the (dance) otter into the (freeze) pond.

....

Synonyms

When you're writing, you often need to use different words for the same thing. They stop your written work from getting dull and boring.

Stuart took a big risk and decided to climb down the big cliff to the big rocks below.

This sentence is much more interesting if you use different words for 'big'.

Stuart took a great risk and decided to climb down the massive cliff to the huge rocks below.

Q1 Fill in each box with words from the list that mean the same thing.

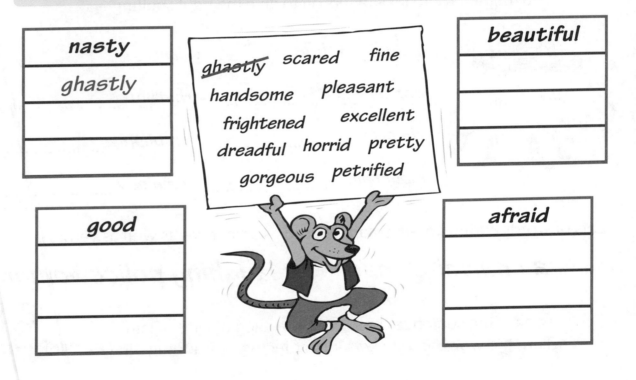

nasty

ghastly

____

____

beautiful

____

____

____

good

____

____

____

afraid

____

____

____

List of words: ~~ghastly~~ scared fine handsome pleasant frightened excellent dreadful horrid pretty gorgeous petrified

Q2 Rewrite these sentences using different words in place of the repeated ones.

The amazing dog started to perform an amazing trick.

....

The pretty Princess arrived at the ball in a pretty dress.

....

Similes

A simile is when you say that a person, place, animal or thing is like something else. Similes always use the word 'as' or the word 'like'.

My lizard is as big as a house.

This tells you what the lizard is like.

Q1 Complete these common similes using the words in the box.

hills   ~~bat~~
post
quiet   tall

As blind as a ___bat___.

As deaf as a _____.

As _____ as a mouse.

As _____ as a tree.   As old as the _____.

Don't forget that some similes use the word '**like**'.

She flew through the air like a rocket.

Q2 Make up your own similes to complete these sentences.

The wolves howled like ___angry ghosts___.

Boris the sheep was as woolly as _____.

Nina crept downstairs as _____ as _____.

The sea was warm like _____, and as blue as _____.

My mum was furious, like _____.

The little singer had a voice like _____.

Gina was as _____ as _____.

Apostrophes

An apostrophe and '-s' shows that something **belongs to** someone.

Randolf's books are amazing.

This shows that the books belong to Randolf.

Q1 Put an apostrophe in the correct place in each sentence.

Everybody wanted to use Graham's computer.

Nobody wanted Samanthas help.

Bens holiday in the jungle was full of surprises.

Toms new records are terrible.

Jonathans party was full of strangers.

If the word ends in '-s' already, you still need to add an apostrophe and another '-s'.

I like Lewis's hat.   Where is Cerys's sister?

If the word ends in '-s' because it is plural, then just put an apostrophe **after** the '-s'.

I saw the lions' den.   I saw the lion's den.

This means there's more than one lion.   This means there's only one lion.

Q2 Put an apostrophe in the correct place in each sentence.
Sometimes you will need to add an '-s' as well.

This scary old place is the Hendersons' house.

Is this the ladies toilet?

James motorbike never seems to work properly.

Chris team-mates think he is great.

There are birds nests all over the forest.

Apostrophes

Q3 Put an apostrophe in the correct place in each of these sentences.

Malcolm found himself clinging to the _cliff's_ edge. cliff

Sophie bought a present for her .... birthday. mum

.... sheep found him a pain. Geoffrey

It was Janice's twin .... birthday. brothers

The .... spaceship had broken down. Martians

The meteorite crashed through the .... roof. Neilsons

You also use apostrophes to fill in for missing letters.
Leave out the extra letters and put an apostrophe in instead.

she has = she's   I am = I'm   we have = we've   you are = you're

Q4 Rewrite these sentences using as many short forms as you can.
Leave out any extra letters and put apostrophes in instead.

It has been a long time since we have eaten any turnips.

It's been a long time since we've eaten any turnips.

You are late. She has been waiting for ages.

....

He has been playing football in his best clothes. He is always getting muddy.

....

I am tired and I have got a headache.

....

Joining Sentences

When you want to add some new information to a sentence,
the easiest thing to do is to put a **full stop** and start a **new sentence**.

I went on the Rocky Mountain ride it was brilliant. ✗

This is a separate bit of information.
It shouldn't carry straight on in the same sentence.

I went on the Rocky Mountain ride. It was brilliant. ✓

Q1 Split these sentences into two separate ones.

a)   Harvey plays tennis he usually plays with Mark.

Harvey plays tennis. He usually plays with Mark.

Split it up!

b)   I had a cheeseburger I had a milkshake as well.

....

c)   Jennifer loves dragons she draws pictures of them.

....

Jennifer

Use words like '**and**' and '**then**' if you want to keep
the new bit of information in the same sentence.

I saw Andy and I told him about the barbecue.

These two bits could
be separate sentences

Q2 Use the most sensible word from the box to join each sentence.

when   because   ~~then~~   where   so

a)   The sheep climbed up the hill, ___then___ they ran down again.

b)   We're going to Scotland .... we'll see some very tall trees.

c)   I'll see you .... I come back from Peru.

d)   I trained hard .... I could compete in the race.

e)   Jason was off school .... he had flu.

English Workbook — Year 4

Joining Sentences

Q3   Use the words below to fill in the gaps in this story.

You'll need some words more than once.

when   but   so that   then   as   and

Martin was a magician. He was usually very good at magic __but__ he had run

out of spells. He went to a magic fair .... he could buy new ones. He

wandered around for a while, ... he saw a stall selling magic vegetables.

A magic beetroot caught his eye .... he picked it up to have a look. He

rubbed it cautiously .... nothing happened.

"You have to switch it on first," said the stallholder .... he saw Martin

struggling. "It takes two batteries," said the stall holder, ... he picked the

beetroot up to demonstrate. He showed Martin all the beetroot's fancy

features .... Martin was very impressed.

"So it turns people into mice .... it tells me the temperature as well?"

You can add extra information on to a sentence with a **comma**. You need to do this if the new bit of information isn't a sentence itself and you're not using a **joining word**.

This is the main bit of the sentence.

The next time I see you, I'll have shorter hair.

This is an extra bit of information saying when I'll have shorter hair.

Q4   Underline the extra bit of information in these sentences. It can come before or after the main part of the sentence.

a)   While we wait for the washing to dry, we can play a game.

b)   I'll go first, if you don't mind.

c)   Oh well, it looks like I've lost.

d)   Next time I play "How many lettuces can I fit up my

jumper", I'll wear a baggier jumper.

More About Present Tense Verbs

Most verbs in the present tense follow a pattern, like the verb 'to take'.

I take   *You take*   *He/She/It takes*
We take   *You take*   *They take*

You add an '-s' with the he/she/it form.

Q1   Finish each sentence with the right form of the verb.

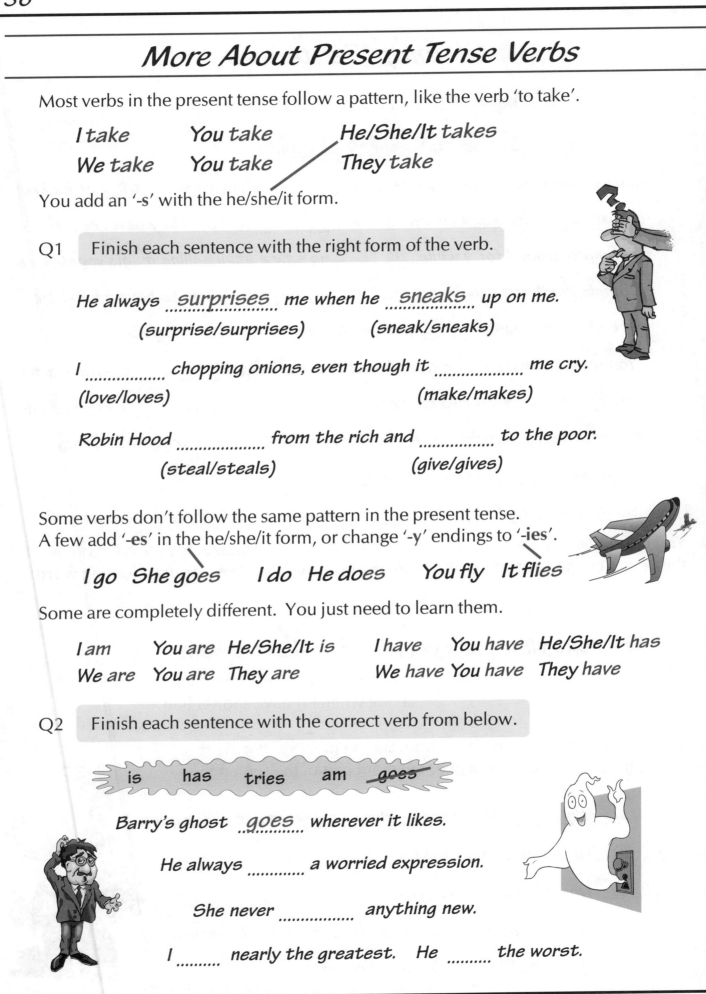

He always ..*surprises*.. me when he ..*sneaks*.. up on me.
        (surprise/surprises)   (sneak/sneaks)

I .... chopping onions, even though it .... me cry.
(love/loves)   (make/makes)

Robin Hood .... from the rich and .... to the poor.
        (steal/steals)   (give/gives)

Some verbs don't follow the same pattern in the present tense.
A few add '-**es**' in the he/she/it form, or change '-**y**' endings to '-**ies**'.

I go   She goes   I do   He does   You fly   It flies

Some are completely different. You just need to learn them.

I am   You are   He/She/It is   I have   You have   He/She/It has
We are   You are   They are   We have   You have   They have

Q2   Finish each sentence with the correct verb from below.

    is   has   tries   am   ~~goes~~

Barry's ghost ..*goes*.. wherever it likes.

He always .... a worried expression.

She never .... anything new.

I .... nearly the greatest.   He .... the worst.

More About Past Tense Verbs

In the past tense most verbs end in '-**ed**'.

cracked, stayed, worked, lifted

Some verbs end in '-**t**' instead of '-**ed**'.
Words like 'sleep' and 'weep' also lose an '**e**' in the past tense.

burnt, smelt, lost, slept, wept

Q3   Finish each sentence with the right past tense form of the verb in brackets.

On the first day, we (stay) ..... stayed ..... in bed till late.

Everybody (sleep) .... really well.

Alan never (leave) .... his deckchair all week.

The rest of us (learn) .... to waterski and skydive.

We (decide) .... to have a barbecue, but Dad (burn) .... the food.

Some verbs are totally irregular in the past. They don't follow any pattern.

go ➔ went,   **do** ➔ did,   **see** ➔ saw,   **have** ➔ had,   **take** ➔ took,   **be** ➔ was

Q4   Complete the story with the past tense form of each verb in brackets.
All the missing verbs are irregular.

Ouch!

I (be) .. was .. in town last weekend, when I (see)

.... Eric. He (have) .... a new pair of

trousers on, but they looked really tight. I (take)

.... him to one side to ask him about them.

"Why (do) .... you buy those trousers, Eric?" I asked. "They're far too tight."

"I (think) .... they might fit me," moaned Eric, "So I tried them on."

"And you still (buy) .... them even though they didn't fit?" I asked, amazed.

"Yes!" (wail) .... Eric, "But only because I can't get them off."

Types of Word

A lot of words in English have the same root, but they change form to become nouns, verbs, adjectives and adverbs.

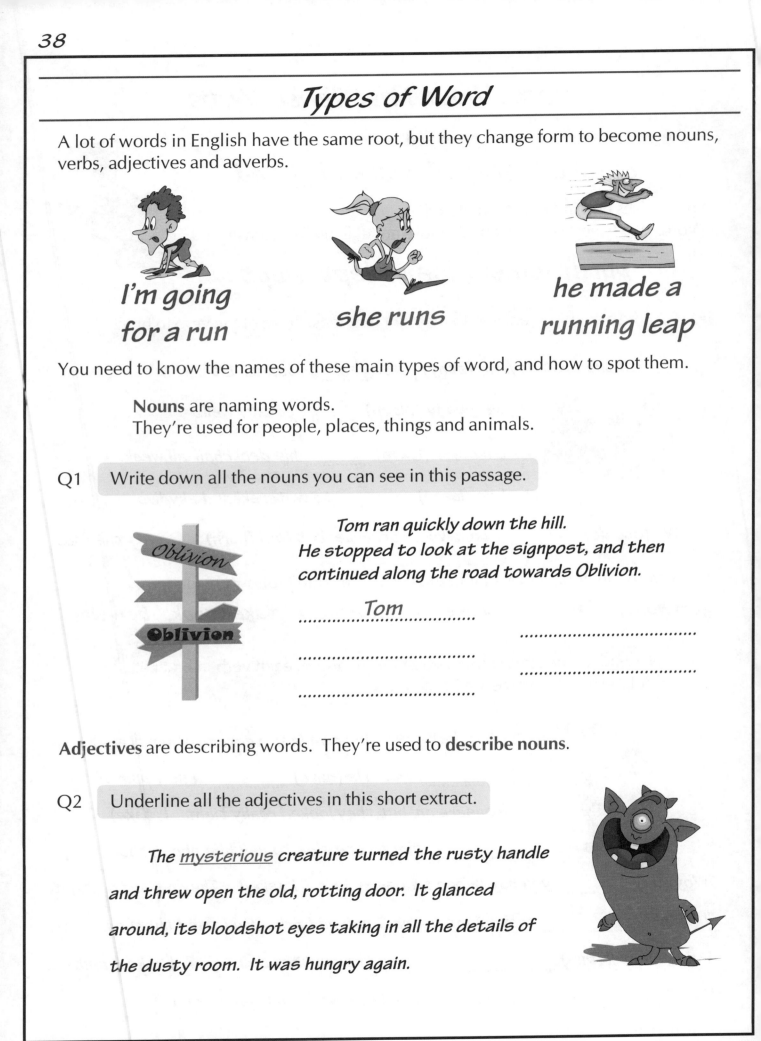

I'm going
for a run

she runs

he made a
running leap

You need to know the names of these main types of word, and how to spot them.

Nouns are naming words.
They're used for people, places, things and animals.

Q1   Write down all the nouns you can see in this passage.

Tom ran quickly down the hill.
He stopped to look at the signpost, and then
continued along the road towards Oblivion.

.... Tom ....

....

....

....

Adjectives are describing words. They're used to **describe nouns**.

Q2   Underline all the adjectives in this short extract.

The <u>mysterious</u> creature turned the rusty handle

and threw open the old, rotting door. It glanced

around, its bloodshot eyes taking in all the details of

the dusty room. It was hungry again.

Types of Word

Don't forget **verbs**. These are the **doing or being words** in a sentence.

Q3 Write down all the verbs you can see in this passage.

> As his beady eyes scanned the room, he saw a dark hole in the middle of the floor. He ran towards it, then dived head first into the opening. He disappeared into the darkness below. He fell a long way until he hit the ground hard at the bottom of the pit. He groaned in pain.

...scanned..., ..., ..., ...,

..................., ..., ..., ...

And remember, an **adverb** describes **a verb** or an **adjective**.

Q4 Circle the adverbs in these sentences.

The tiger ran (quickly) after him.

The little mice were amazingly fast.

A nasty man sneakily stole my vast collection of music.

The mammoth fell hard on the slippery glacier.

Q5 Find three nouns, three verbs, three adjectives and three adverbs in this passage. Write them in columns underneath.

> Once upon a time, there was a very pretty young Princess. One day, her parents told her she was going to marry a local Prince.
> Two days before the wedding, a terribly nasty witch turned the Prince into an ugly frog. He hopped sadly into the royal chamber and croakingly begged the Princess to kiss him better.

Nouns	Verbs	Adjectives	Adverbs
time	was	pretty	very

Punctuation

There's a lot more to punctuation than just full stops and commas.
There are **semi-colons**, **colons** and **hyphens** too. They all help to make your writing **easier** to understand and more **interesting** to read.

Semi-colon: **;**   colon: **:**   dash: ▬   hyphen: ▬

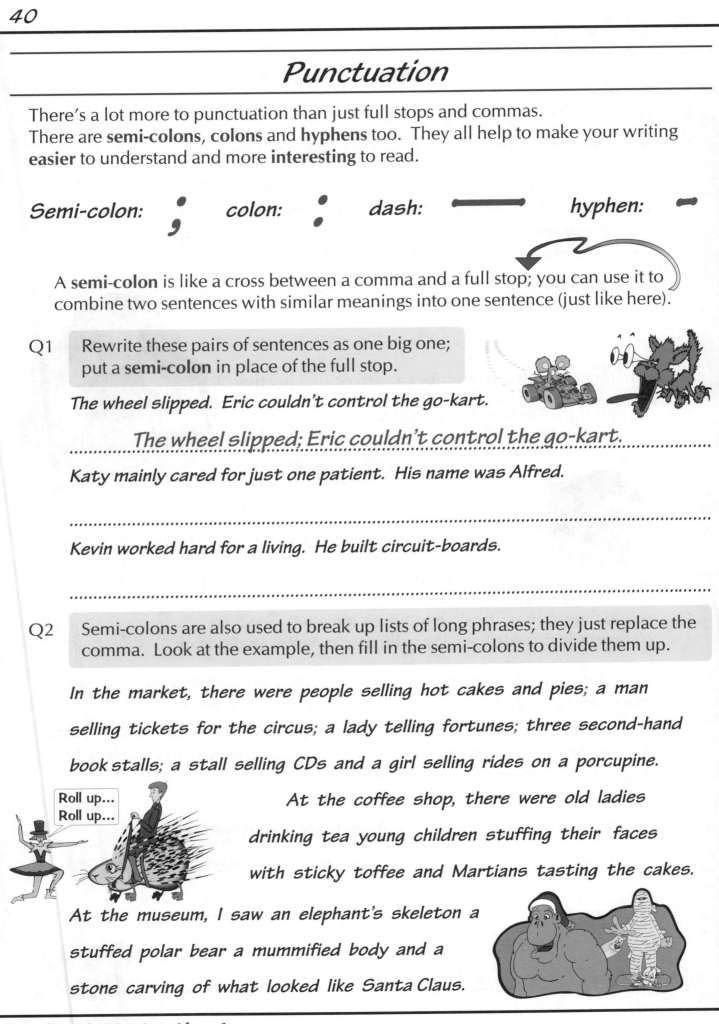

A **semi-colon** is like a cross between a comma and a full stop; you can use it to combine two sentences with similar meanings into one sentence (just like here).

Q1   Rewrite these pairs of sentences as one big one; put a **semi-colon** in place of the full stop.

The wheel slipped. Eric couldn't control the go-kart.

The wheel slipped; Eric couldn't control the go-kart.

Katy mainly cared for just one patient. His name was Alfred.

....

Kevin worked hard for a living. He built circuit-boards.

....

Q2   Semi-colons are also used to break up lists of long phrases; they just replace the comma. Look at the example, then fill in the semi-colons to divide them up.

In the market, there were people selling hot cakes and pies; a man selling tickets for the circus; a lady telling fortunes; three second-hand book stalls; a stall selling CDs and a girl selling rides on a porcupine.

At the coffee shop, there were old ladies drinking tea young children stuffing their faces with sticky toffee and Martians tasting the cakes.

Roll up...
Roll up...

At the museum, I saw an elephant's skeleton a stuffed polar bear a mummified body and a stone carving of what looked like Santa Claus.

Punctuation

A **colon** is used to **introduce a list**; it shows that the list is about to begin.

Q3 Write in the colon in the following sentences.

You need these ingredients: olive oil, flour, water, garlic and cheese.

Don't forget these things tent, sleeping bag, boots, torch, map and compass.

Barbados is wonderful sun, surf, sea, white sand, cold drinks and coconuts.

Colons are **also used** when the second part of a sentence **explains** the first part, or gives extra information. A **dash** can be used in exactly the **same** way as a colon.

Q4 Use either a dash or a colon to make these sentences clearer.

Exercise — it's good for you, honest!

Computers are the future they're the way forward.

Visit South America see Inca ruins, rainforests and the Andes.

Hyphens are used to **link words** together to **change their meaning**, or just to add sense to the phrase. Some words — like numbers — always have a hyphen (like twenty-one).

Q5 Use hyphens to sort out the phrases in the sentences below. The meaning should change from what you see in the picture on the left, to what you see in the picture on the right.

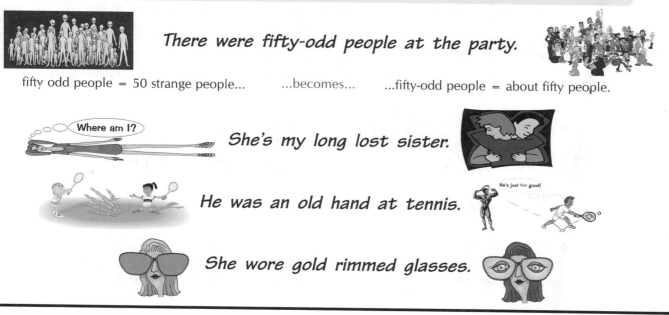

There were fifty-odd people at the party.

fifty odd people = 50 strange people...   ...becomes...   ...fifty-odd people = about fifty people.

She's my long lost sister.

He was an old hand at tennis.

She wore gold rimmed glasses.

Common Letter Strings

Some words look and sound similar. They have some **letters** in common.

give live   dove glove

Here both words have **-ive** in common, and both words here have **-ove** in common.

Q1   Match up each of the words on the left with a word on the right that looks and sounds the same.

tough	boot
gull	rough
root	look
weight	eight
meat	trough
hook	seat
cough	dull

Unfortunately, there are also some words which have letters in common but **don't** sound the same; they only **look** like they make the same sound.

move love   cost post

These words don't sound the same. Neither do these words.

Q2   Look at the lists of words with letters in common below.
In each list, circle the word that looks the same but doesn't sound the same.

boot	root	foot	pour	sour	hour
match	watch	catch	crow	blow	now
bear	hear	dear	move	love	glove
cone	one	bone	some	dome	home
lost	post	cost	vase	case	base

Common Letter Strings

There are some letter strings with **more than two** ways of saying them.

tough through plough cough

None of these words is said the same way, even though they all **look** similar.

Q3 | Look at these words and draw lines to match up words with the same sound and the same letter string.

I said pour, not poor...

hour   should
                    dour

knave   four   gave
weight   could   save   pour

        freight   sour   would

        shove   dove

eight   wave

love   shave

Q4 | Write a short sentence using each pair of words below. Each pair has a common letter string.

snow, cow   *The cow watched the snow falling.*

moth, mother ....

office, mice ....

line, machine ....

Don't forget that some words sound the same but are spelt differently. They don't have common letter strings, they just **rhyme**.

To rhyme is not a crime

But stealing's not appealing

Q5 | Think of words that rhyme with each of the **purple** words below. See if you can fill all the spaces.

bone	snow	boot	match
moan	so	....	....
....	....	....	....
....	....	....	....

Speech Marks

You use speech marks with things that people are actually saying.

"I found it," said Patricia.

This is what Patricia said, so you need to put speech marks around it.

Q1 A bit of speech can come at the beginning or the end of a sentence. Put speech marks in the correct places for each of these sentences.

"I'll stay," said Mandy.

Gary yelled, "Look out!"

I hate shopping, cried Sophie.

The giant growled, I'm hungry!

Don't forget to put commas and full stops in the right places with speech marks too.

If the bit of speech is at the start of the sentence, put a comma at the end of it.

"I need some help," said Ed.

The comma comes before the speech mark.

If the bit of speech is at the end, put a comma before the first speech mark, and a full stop before the last one.

Ed said, "I need some help."

Here's the comma.   And here's the full stop.

Q2 Put commas and full stops in the right places for each of these sentences.

"I lost a fiver," said Robin.   Tracy complained, "It's too hot."

Sheila whispered "You're late"   "Please explain" said Mr Jones

James replied "I got lost, Sir"   "I don't believe you" said Boris

Speech Marks

Always remember to start any bit of speech with a capital letter.

"Come here," said Sue.   Sue said, "Come here."

Even when the speech starts in the middle of the sentence, it still has a capital letter.

Q3 Look at these sentences containing bits of speech. Write them out again. Put capital letters, speech marks and commas in the correct places.

Cliff asked why does no one like me?

Cliff asked, "Why does no one like me?"

I didn't know that said Lena.

....

Sam replied everybody knows that!

....

The rats said where's the food?

....

Sometimes a sentence can have two bits of speech.
It follows the same rules for speech marks and commas.

"Nobody will ever find out," he muttered, "who the thief really was!"

These three bits are all part of one sentence.

Q4 Put commas and speech marks in the correct places in each sentence.

"It's a long shot," said Pete, "but it might just work."

The murderer said Shirley Holmes was you!

There must be a way she whispered of escaping from this cage.

Types of Sentence

There are four types of sentence: statements, questions, orders and exclamations.
A statement gives information:

This is Leeds.   We've made mud-pies.

A question asks something.

Why are we here?   Who won the match?

Q1   Look at each sentence and say whether it is a **statement** or a **question**.

Yes, but I prefer...
Ships!

Do you like chips?   ...question......

You are always late.   ....

How do you do?   ....

Is it time to go?   ....

It is time to go.   ....

An order tells somebody to do something.

Go away.   Don't do that!

An exclamation is a sentence that shows strong feelings.

That's brilliant!   What a good idea!

Q2   Look at each sentence and decide whether it is a **statement**,
an **order**, a **question** or an **exclamation**.

It was awful!   ...exclamation...

Come with me.   ....

Who pulled the plug? ....

What a day!   ....

It was raining.   ....

Types of Sentence

You can change one type of sentence into another.
A statement can be turned into a question.

It is raining.   Is it raining?

Here's the statement.   Put the verb first and add a question mark.

Q3   Change these statements into questions.

You are happy.   *Are you happy?*

It was a good day.   ....

We were late.   ....

Elvis is hungry.   ....

Sometimes you have to change the verb and add a new word to make a question.

We lost the game.   Did we lose the game?

Change 'lost' to 'lose' and put 'did' on the front to make a question.

Q4   Turn these statements into questions.
Don't forget to change the verb to a present tense.

They did it.   *Did they do it?*

You wanted to go.   *Did you want to go?*

We came last.   ....

She ate the worms.   ....

I saw her.   ....

You felt sick.   ....

Andrei bounced a million times on his pogo-stick.

....

More Suffixes

One really common suffix is **-able**. It's added to some verbs to make adjectives.

-able   spreadable

Spreadable cheese
New!
Kids love it!

Q1   Match up these words with their meanings.

disposable   is fun

unstoppable   can be worn

enjoyable   can be broken

wearable   can't be stopped

breakable   can be thrown away

This unstoppable train is very enjoyable!

Watch out — some words have the suffix **-ible**.   **-ible**
It sounds the same as **-able**, but it's spelt differently.

Sometimes, when you take off the suffix you aren't left with a proper word.

edible   ed ible   ed   eat

'Ed' isn't a proper word, but it sounds a bit like 'eat'. You can guess what it means.

Q2   Match up these words with their meanings.

edible   can be turned inside out

reversible   can be got into

accessible   can be bent

visible   can be eaten

flexible   can be seen

My bendy liquorice suitcases are flexible, reversible, accessible, visible and edible.

Q3   Fill in the gaps with the correct form, **-ible** or **-able**.

poss_ible_ ....   flamm...........   mov..........

reli...........   indestruct...........   unbeliev..........

incred...........   sens...........   avail..........

renew...........   adjust...........   inflat..........

More Suffixes

Most words ending in **-ive** are adjectives.

distinctive　　　*expensive*

Q4 Fill in the gaps in these sentences.

> talkative　　~~intensive~~
> massive　　　impressive

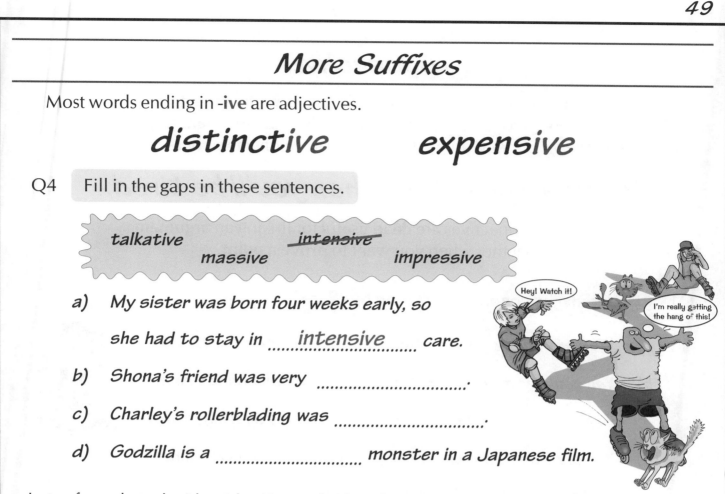

a) My sister was born four weeks early, so

   she had to stay in ......*intensive*...... care.

b) Shona's friend was very ....

c) Charley's rollerblading was ....

d) Godzilla is a .... monster in a Japanese film.

Lots of words end with a 'shun' sound. The 'shun' sound can be spelled '**sion**' or '**tion**'.

repulsion

caution

CAUTION
FLAMMABLE
LIQUIDS

Q5 Should it be **-tion** or **-sion**? Finish each sentence with the correct form.

I have been known to lose my temper, on occa *sion* .

Fric.......... happens when things rub together.

The Norman inva.............. took place in 1066.

Americans say vaca.............. instead of holiday.

Varia......... means how much difference there is.

Educa......... means learning new things.

Loca.............. is another word for place.

The surgeon will perform the opera.............. .

Connectives

Connectives are words and phrases that **join** bits of writing **together**.
They can join things together in a **sentence** or they can join **paragraphs**
together in bigger bits of writing. **If** and **then** are connectives here.

If you stay up late then you'll be tired.

Connectives are **dead useful** for linking an **argument**
together when you want to **prove a point**.

Q1   Underline the **connectives** in each sentence.

a)   We went to the park on Thursday <u>and</u> we had a brilliant time.

b)   You could write her a letter or you could send her an email.

c)   Sean is good at thinking up stories, but his spelling is awful.

d)   You shouldn't eat out of the pan because it's bad manners.

   On the other hand, it saves washing up a plate.

Q2   **Draw an arrow** to match each phrase on the left to the **best ending**.

a)   <u>We had to leave one
suitcase behind</u>

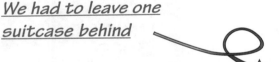

about me in her diary.

b)   Kevin was surprised

<u>because it didn't fit in the car</u>.

about giant, green hairy bugs.

c)   I couldn't believe
what she wrote

until it was time for tea.

d)   The lads and I played football

when the baby took his ice lolly.

What's the buzz, Geoffrey?

Quit bugging me!

e)   Geoffrey kept
having nightmares

Hey!

Connectives

a)   The Eurostar gets to Paris in under 3 hours,   and I bought a huge courgette.
however, it is expensive.

b)   The rope got weaker and weaker.   Finally, it gave way altogether.
Then we had a cup of tea.

c)   If you don't learn your times tables,   you'll never be really good at Maths.
they will fall down.

d)   The belt has come out of my trousers,   and I'm going to Peru.
so they might fall down.

> This will mean that   The reason for   however
>
> so   Unfortunately   looking at it another way   If

There are plans to cut the number of bus routes in Borsetshire.

__This will mean that__ people in remote areas of the county will have to use cars to travel to work and to the shops.

............................, cars pollute the air, ... many people think that people should use their cars less often. With these new plans, ... , people will be forced to use their cars more often.

.... cancelling the buses is that not enough people use them to pay for the cost of running them. This is true, but ....

..............................., perhaps most people don't know when the buses run.

.... people knew when there was a bus that could take them to work or into town, they would be able to choose whether to use their cars or not.

Its and It's

Its and it's are actually totally **different** words. A lot of people get them muddled up.

Pick it up by its handle.   I can't, it's heavy.

Its means 'belonging to it'.
Its **doesn't** have an apostrophe.

It's is short for 'it is' here.
It can also mean 'it has'.

Q1   Fill in the gaps in each sentence.

a)   Make sure the dog is on ....*its*.... lead.

b)   The plan to have free coffee seems like a good idea.

.... only drawback is that we might completely run out of coffee.

c)   Some people say that the CD has had .... day.

It's is short for **it is** or **it has**. There's an **apostrophe** to show that letters are missed out.

Q2   Fill in the gaps in these sentences.

a)   ...*It's*.... been raining cats and dogs and rabbits all day.

b)   "She started it!" wailed Emma. "Miss, ... not fair!"

c)   This jacket's really cool. .... got three hidden pockets on the inside.

Q3   Underline the the right word (**it's** or **its**) in each sentence.

a)   Sarah's cat is scared of (its/it's) own shadow,

and she thinks (its/it's) silly.

b)   My computer lost some of (its/it's) files today.

(Its/It's) really annoying when it does that.

c)   My dog thinks (its/it's) a cow. It likes to eat grass,

and it won't touch (its/it's) dog food.

d)   We just bought a new television. (Its/It's) brilliant. (Its/It's) got

surround sound, which is awesome when you're watching a film.

Compound Words

Compound words are made up of other **smaller words**.

goldfish

Goldfish **sounds** like
gold and fish.

cupboard

Cupboard **doesn't** sound
like cup and board.

Some compound words **don't** sound like they're made of two words.
But knowing that they are made up of two little words makes them **easier** to **spell**.

Q1   Underline the correct spelling of the words in brackets.

    a)   If it's not on the table, look in the (<u>cupboard</u>/cuboard).

    b)   On a ship, port is left and (starboard/starbard) is right.

    c)   Barbara blows her nose in a blue (handkerchief/hankerchief).

    d)   A (shepard/shepherd) is someone who looks after sheep.

    e)   Wicked Wanda wears a (necklace/necklass) of bat's teeth.

    f)   I like curried cabbage and fish pie for (breakfast/brekfast).

The ending **-less** often sounds more like **-luss**. Think of it as '**less**' to help with spelling.

Q2   Fill in the gaps in each sentence.

    a)   Ted is hope<u>less</u>..... at Maths. He can't get his head round sums at all.

    b)   This pencil is use......... The lead keeps on breaking.

    c)   It's no good watering that plant — it looks completely life.........

    d)   "Sense.......... hooligans!" shouted the old man.

Some **place names** and people's **surnames** are compound words.
They aren't usually spelt the same way that they're said.

Q3   Add **-ford**, **-son** or **-man** to these words to make a common surname
    or the name of a well-known place.

    Robert<u>son</u>   Gold........   Guild........   Ox.............

    Robin.......   John........   Richard........   Brad.............

Diminutives

Diminutives are 'short' forms of words, or words used to show something is small.

Danny Dan   kitchenette

These are short forms of Daniel.   a **little** kitchen

Q1 Underline the diminutives in these sentences.

The waiters gave us hot <u>towelettes</u> so we could wipe our hands.

Mighty oaks grow from tiny saplings.

We planted the seedlings in compost.

Our school has just bought a minibus.

> Watch out — sapling is a diminutive, but it means **little tree**, not little sap.

Some diminutives mean something different from the original word.

leaf   leaflet

> Wordlets? Wordlings? Wordettes? Miniwords?

Q2 Choose a prefix or suffix from the book to make these words into diminutives.

> mini- -ette -let

flannel   _flannelette_   leaf   ....

owl   ....   bus   ....

cab   ....   cover   ....

Q3 People's nicknames are often diminutives.
For each of these names, write a diminutive version.

Daniel   _Danny_   Benjamin   ....

Thomas   ....   Joanne   ....

Alexander   ....   Louise   ....

Margaret   ....   James   ....

Alliteration

Alliteration is when nearby words start with the same **consonant** sound.

Stop sticking stamps on Steven!

This sentence repeats the st sound.

Q1 Underline the letters that alliterate in these sentences.

a) <u>B</u>etty put a <u>b</u>it of <u>b</u>itter <u>b</u>utter in her <u>b</u>atter and made her <u>b</u>atter <u>b</u>itter.

b) It's got a totally terrific tangy taste!

c) Summer is the season when we see the sun.

d) Philip found Fiona's phone number.

e) Wendy wore one wonky wellington and one washed-out sock.

Q2 Add another word that alliterates with the three already there.

dark dangerous desperate ......*dog*......

pattern purse purple ....

stalk stop stupid ....

choose cheese chips ....

bald barmy batsman ....

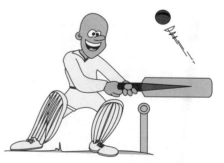

Q3 Use the words in the box to fill in the gaps in this passage.

> pure   sloppy   pint   plastic   ~~sat~~

Sam ......*sat*...... on his seat and sang for his supper. He poured a

.... of perfectly .... water into his glass. Next, he

sloshed .... spaghetti sauce onto his .... plate.

Prefixes and Suffixes

Don't forget that **prefixes** and **suffixes** change the meaning of a root word.

hope + ful = hopeful   ('hope' is the root word here)

Q1 Underline the **prefixes** and **suffixes** in these words.

<u>un</u>usual<u>ly</u>

monosyllabic

mathematically

inconclusive   antibiotic

uneconomical   postponement

undisciplined   distressingly

If you don't know what one of these words means, use the prefixes, suffixes and word root to work it out.

Q2 Verbs that end in a **silent -e** lose the -e before adding a **suffix**. Fill in these word sums.

a)   vibrate + tion = ...

b)   translate + tion = ...

c)   create + tion = ...

d)   dedicate + tion = ...

e)   navigate + ion = ...

Q3 Use the words in the box to fill in the blanks. Look at the clues in each sentence to help you.

pessimist   unhopeful   ~~competitive~~
repossession   disproportionate

Andy, they're repossessing your house!

A ....competitive.... person likes to play to win.

A .... is ....

.... is a fancy word for "taking something back from you".

If something isn't in proportion it is ....

Prefixes and Suffixes

Q4 Add suffixes from the box to complete these words.

| ful | ation | tic | ly | ic | al |

a) Joanne uses an inhaler because she's asthma _tic_.

b) My kitten, Betsy, is very play ....:

c) Snow White is a fiction ...... character.

d) Daniel's dad likes reading histor .... novels.

e) All cows do is stare dumb .... at you and moo.

f) The import .... of live tortoises is illegal.

g) Sue does everything method ....:

Hint: this one needs **two** suffixes.

Hint: this one needs **three** suffixes!

Q5 Use the prefixes and suffixes in the box to fill in the gaps in this passage.

| -tions | -al | -hood | -ship | -tion | -ian | re- | -ic | -ical |

Class 4T went on an education_al_ visit to the town museum.

They had been studying life in Victor ...... times in their History

lessons and they had written a short project called "A Victorian

Child ....". The museum has a lot of informa ....corded

and collected by local people.

Class 4T found out that Victor ..... children lived

in very different condi ...... from children today. The

soci ...... and econom ..... differences between rich and

poor were much greater then. Poor children often

worked in mines and factories, sometimes in

diabol ...... condi ....

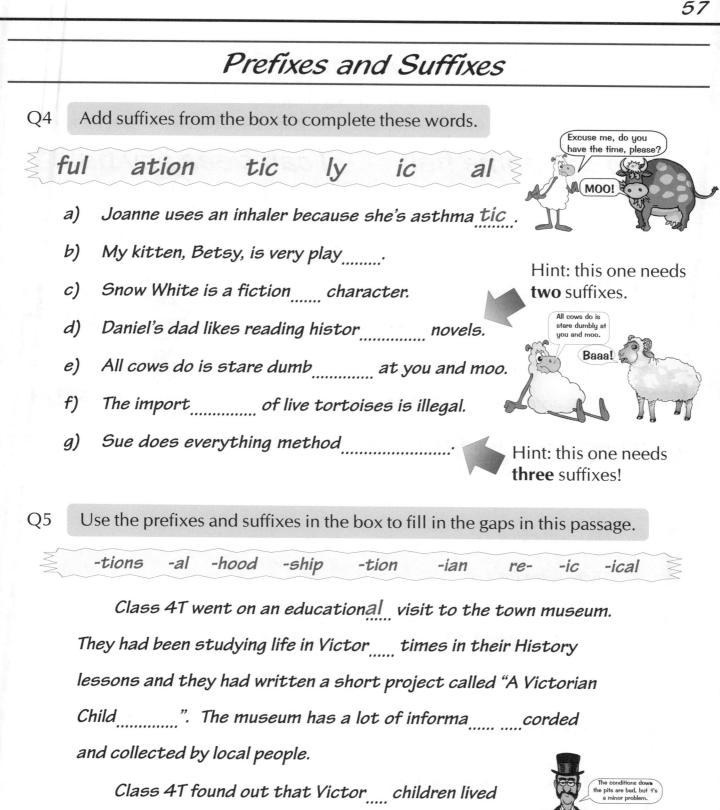

58

Positive and Negative Sentences

Positive sentences say what something **is**, **has** or **does**.
Negative sentences say the opposite. They use words like **not**, **isn't**, **can't** and **no**.

I can see some fish.   *I can't see any fish.*

This word has changed, too.

Q1 Put a tick by the sentence if it's positive and a cross if it's negative.

a) *The doctor looked at my ankle.* ✓

b) *Sunil plays chess with the Queen of Sweden.*

c) *Esther hasn't got a coat on.*

d) *There aren't any jelly babies left.*

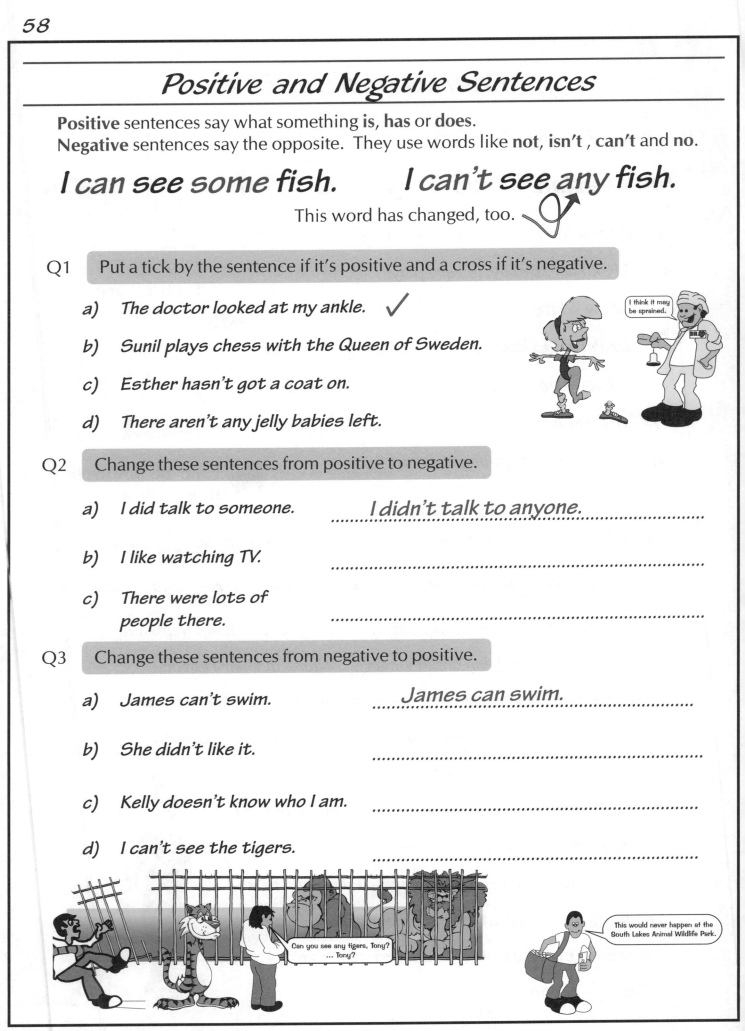

I think it may be sprained.

Q2 Change these sentences from positive to negative.

a) *I did talk to someone.* .... *I didn't talk to anyone.* ....

b) *I like watching TV.* ....

c) *There were lots of people there.* ....

Q3 Change these sentences from negative to positive.

a) *James can't swim.* .... *James can swim.* ....

b) *She didn't like it.* ....

c) *Kelly doesn't know who I am.* ....

d) *I can't see the tigers.* ....

Can you see any tigers, Tony? ... Tony?

This would never happen at the South Lakes Animal Wildlife Park.

Answers

P1 ALPHABETICAL ORDER

Q1
Billy, Corey, Kerry, Molly;
Fred, Gareth, Lucy, Michelle,
Peter;
Anil, Becky, David, Jayne, Jenny;
Chewie, Han, Leia, Luke,
Obi-Wan

Q2
cabbage, cave, chance, chap,
church, coffee; lady, lamb,
lamp, later, lava, llama;
anorak, ant, antifreeze,
apartment, apatosaurus, apple

Q3
Brenda, Brian, Bruce, Brunhilda;
Janet, Jasmine, Jaswinder, Jayne,
Zorg; Michael, Michelle, Mike,
Mina, Miroslav

P2 VERBS

Q1
went, had, stayed, gave, slept,
found, was sleeping

Q2
I am having a few computer
problems.
It is very sunny.
Jane has a letter to post.

Q3
I will try to finish my book.
Harry will go to Nottingham.
We will sing Christmas carols.
It will rain.

P3 VERBS

Q4
Wrap one ice-cube in paper,
one in foil and one in
cheesecake. Leave them on a
plate. Look at them every 2
minutes and write down the
time when each one melts.
Compare the results.

Q5
Today started off bright and
sunny. There was... some
ground frost which melted by
mid-morning. There was a cold
wind from the West, which
brought some cloud. It rained
chocolate drops in the
afternoon. The temperatures
were between 5 and 10 degrees
Celsius.

P4 DOUBLE LETTERS

Q1
bubble, hotter, fatter; middle,
battle, rotten; apple, horrid,
cattle

Q2
a) squirrels, common
b) bottles
c) bubbles
d) waddles

Q3
saddle, middle, ripples, rubble,
rotten

P5 HOMOPHONES

Q1
a) too, b) two, c) too, d) to

Q2
a) piece, b) peace, c) pieces,
d) Pieces

Q3
a) they're, b) there, c) their,
d) they're, there, e) they're

**P6 REGULAR AND
IRREGULAR VERBS**

Q1
picked, played, appeared,
shouted

Q2
chipped, ripped, patted, digging

Q3
found, were, said, thought,
caught, fought

**P7 REGULAR AND
IRREGULAR VERBS**

Q4
I caught the bus at half past
eight.
Sally couldn't come to the party.
Terry bought oranges.
Roland rang his mates on his
mobile phone.

Q5
woke up, was sleeping, looked,
was, jumped, ran, staggered,
laughed, asked, realised
...or any suitable answers.

P8 SUFFIXES

Q1
happiness, sadness, illness;
adulthood, childhood,
parenthood; leadership,
companionship, friendship;
amazement, amusement,
excitement

Q2
original, customary, realistic,
musical, personal, dietary,
artistic, cautionary

P9 SUFFIXES

Q3
neighbourhood, kindness,
membership, fairness,
partnership, knighthood,
premiership

Q4
majestic, argument, likelihood,
laziness

P10 PHONEMES

Q1
a) slip, b) sit, c) flaw,
d) jug, e) rid

Q2
grow, fish, bread, claw, food,
howl, pull, holiday

Q3
care — spare, rare; fly — why, tie;
lip — strip, clip; hair — blare,
where; star — car, bar
...or any suitable answers.

P11 RHYMES

Q1
deer — hill
back — slip
mouse — claw
lip — ear
mill — house
saw — track

Q2
young, fly, free, holes

**P12 MAKING VERBS FROM
OTHER WORDS**

Q1
familiarize, thicken, shorten,
finalize

Q2
liquidize, strengthen, equalize,
deaden, quicken

Q3
madden, thicken, harden,
soften, forbidden, gladden

**P13 MAKING VERBS FROM
OTHER WORDS**

Q4
falsify — false
beautify — beauty
terrify — terror
codify — code
horrify — horror
uglify — ugly

Q5
widen, solidify, personalize,
sadden, equalize, justify

P14 ADVERBS

Q1
carefully, dimly, slowly,
stealthily, wildly, soundlessly,
safely, suddenly, angrily, really

Q2
sleepily, closely, swiftly,
cheerfully, faintly, gracefully

P15 ADVERBS

Q3
a) clumsily describes climbed
b) endlessly describes rained
c) dangerously describes loose
d) painfully describes scraped
e) greedily describes lapped

Q4
brightly, dimly, brilliantly;
quickly, swiftly, slowly;
perfectly, tightly, loosely

P16 DESCRIPTIVE VERBS

Q1
a) go, dash, skip, run
b) run, sprint, dash, hurry
c) eat, munch, gobble,
consume
d) hit, strike, punch, clobber
e) take, remove, capture, seize
...or any suitable answers.

Q2
a) glanced, b) glared, glared,
c) peered

Q3
a) slurping, b) biting,
c) chewing

P17 DESCRIPTIVE VERBS

Q4
a) grabbed, b) dashed, ran,
c) hurled, d) limped,
e) pinched, f) sped

Q5
peered, sniffed, stank, reeked,
nibbled, gulped, mopped,
wishing, munching, appreciate

P18 COMMAS

Q1
a) Bratley Shields was playing at
the Palladium, so we went to
see her.
b) We waited outside the
Palladium for hours, and we
met lots of people.
c) We saw Bratley, but we didn't
get her autograph.

Q2
a) Sam and Anna visited
PenguinWorld, the world's best
penguin park.
b) They went in the Arena of
Ice, the home of thirty Emperor
penguins.
c) They liked all the rides,
especially the Big Penguin
Twister.
d) The next time they're at the
South Pole, they'll be visiting
PenguinWorld again.

Q3
a) When I'm hungry, I have a
bowl of huckleberry flakes.
b) I like cereal, especially
huckleberry flakes.
c) Huckleberry flakes taste
delicious, which is why I like
them.
d) When I run out of
huckleberry flakes, I rush to buy
more.

P19 COMMAS

Q4
a) Dr Brookes and Mrs Johnson,
the receptionist, are doing a
sponsored run.
b) Billy, who'd never played
Frogball before, won the prize.
c) Barbara Brolly, the weather
forecaster, is opening the new
supermarket.
d) I saw Dave, whose grandad
invented flavoured crisps, eating
plain crisps.
e) Flavoured crisps, as Dave's
grandad used to say, are the
best.

Q5
Next week, I'm going to Canada
to see my aunt and uncle. It's a
long flight, about 8 hours, so I'll
be really tired. When I get there,
I'll probably go straight to bed.
My uncle, who's a fireman, is
going to show me around. I'm
looking forward to seeing all the
sights, especially Niagara Falls.
Hopefully, he'll take me to an
ice hockey game, which is
something I've never done
before. I'm going to take loads
of photos, just so you can see
what my trip to Canada was like.

P20 SYLLABLES

Q1
doctor, thousand, happiness,
giraffe, piano, silly

Q2
1, 2, 2, 2, 4, 3

Q3
rec + ord, sha + dow, con +
fus + ing, mes + sag + es
...or any suitable answers.

**P21 'I' BEFORE 'E' AND
'E' BEFORE 'I'**

Q1
field, shield, friend, believe,
piece, niece, siege, achieve,
brief

Q2
ceiling, receive, conceit,
science, deceive, perceive

Q3
Check for spelling errors.

P22 ADJECTIVES

Q1
youthful, old, ancient;
tiny, small, big, enormous;
OK, good, fantastic

Q2
cat — quite small, mouse —
small, fly — very small, amoeba
— extremely small

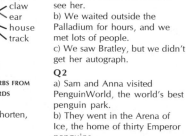

P23 ADJECTIVES

Q3
tall, taller, tallest;
weak, weaker, weakest;
great, greater, greatest;
cool, cooler, coolest

Q4
more awkward, most awkward;
more beautiful, most beautiful;
more terrified, most terrified

Q5
large, huge, gigantic;
quite cold, very cold,
extremely cold;
tricky, hard, impossible

P24 GENDER WORDS

Q1
masculine: king, fox, uncle,
brother, boy, son / feminine:
sister, vixen, daughter, queen,
girl, aunt

Q2
tigress, sir, uncle,
headmistress, duchess, witch,
king, nephew

Q3
daughter, her; She, niece;
Princess; cow

P25 OLD WORDS

Q1
frock
wireless
wigging
flying machine

Q2
radio; food; wicked; bloke;
nonsense; bet
...or any suitable answers.

P26 DEFINITIONS

Q1
windmill — a kind of factory
that uses wind to make the
machinery work;
microwave oven — an
electronic oven that cooks food
very quickly;
comedian — someone who
entertains people by making
them laugh

Q2
cat — a small furry animal, with
four legs, kept as a pet; roller
skate — a shoe, with wheels, for
moving over smooth ground;
guitar — a musical instrument,
with strings, played with the
fingers

Q3
... any suitable answers.

P26 DEFINITIONS

Q4
wardrobe — large, bedroom,
cupboard, clothes; plum — soft,
juicy, fruit, stone; parrot —
noisy, colourful, bird, tropical

Q5
wardrobe — large bedroom
clothes cupboard — large
clothes cupboard — clothes
cupboard — cupboard; plum
— soft juicy purple fruit — soft
juicy fruit — juicy fruit — fruit;
parrot — noisy, colourful,
tropical bird — colourful,
tropical bird — tropical bird —
bird
...or any suitable answers.

Answers are always given column by column, not row by row.

Answers

P28 FORMING ADJECTIVES

Q1
hopeful, heroic, roadworthy, shocking, careful, hairy

Q2
tasty, careful, senseless, hungry, caring, graceful, loving, stripey

P29 FORMING ADJECTIVES

Q3
broken, electrical, careless, spinning

Q4
acidic, dangerous, ridiculous, mountainous; villainous, rhythmic, economic, melodic

Q5
The singing frog loved to play the piano.; The daring climber was stuck in a frightening position.; Lucy followed the dancing otter into the freezing pond.

P30 SYNONYMS

Q1
nasty, ghastly, dreadful, horrid; good, excellent, fine, pleasant; beautiful, gorgeous, pretty, handsome; afraid, scared, petrified, frightened

Q2
...any suitable answers.

P31 SIMILES

Q1
As blind as a bat, As deaf as a post, As quiet as a mouse, As tall as a tree, As old as the hills

Q2
...any suitable answers.

P32 APOSTROPHES

Q1
Everybody wanted to use Graham's computer.; Nobody wanted Samantha's help.; Ben's holiday to the jungle was full of surprises.; Tom's new records are terrible.; Jonathan's party was full of strangers.

Q2
This scary old place is the Hendersons' house.; Is this the ladies' toilet?; James's motorbike never seemed to work properly.; Chris's team-mates think he is great.; There are birds' nests all over the forest.

P33 APOSTROPHES

Q3
Malcolm found himself clinging to the cliff's edge.; Sophie bought a present for her mum's birthday.; Geoffrey's sheep found him a pain.; It was Janice's twin brothers' birthday.; The Martians' spaceship had broken down.; The meteorite crashed through the Neilsons' roof.

Q4
It's been a long time since we've eaten any turnips.; You're late. She's been waiting for ages.; He's been playing football in his best clothes. He's always getting muddy.; I'm tired and I've got a headache.

P34 JOINING SENTENCES

Q1
a) Harvey plays tennis. He usually plays with Mark.

b) I had a cheeseburger. I had a milkshake as well.

c) Jennifer loves dragons. She draws pictures of them.

Q2
a) then, b) where, c) when, d) so, e) because

P35 JOINING SENTENCES

Q3
but, so that, then, and, but, when, as, and, and
...or any suitable answers.

Q4
a) While we wait for the washing to dry, we can play a game.
b) I'll go first, if you don't mind.
c) Oh well, it looks like I've lost.
d) Next time I play, "How many lettuces can I fit up my jumper," I'll wear a baggier jumper.

P36 MORE ABOUT PRESENT TENSE VERBS

Q1
surprises, sneaks; love, makes; steals, gives

Q2
ghost, has, tries, am, is

P37 MORE ABOUT PAST TENSE VERBS

Q3
stayed, slept, left, learnt, decided, burnt

Q4
was, saw, had, took, did, thought, bought, wailed

P38 TYPES OF WORD

Q1
Tom, hill, signpost, road, Oblivion

Q2
mysterious, rusty, old, rotting, bloodshot, dusty.

P39 TYPES OF WORD

Q3
scanned, saw, ran, dived, disappeared, fell, hit, groaned

Q4
quickly, amazingly, sneakily, hard

Q5
Any three of these nouns...
time, years, Princess, day, parents, Prince, days, wedding, witch, (Prince), frog, chamber, (Princess)
Any three of these verbs...
was, told, going, marry, turned, hopped, begged, kiss
Any three of these adjectives..
pretty, young, local, nasty, ugly, royal
Any three of these adverbs...
very, terribly, sadly, croakingly

P40 PUNCTUATION

Q1
The wheel slipped; Eric couldn't control the go-kart. Katy mainly cared for one patient; his name was Alfred. Kevin worked hard for a living; he built circuit-boards.

Q2
In the market, there were people selling hot cakes and pies; a man selling tickets for the circus; a lady telling fortunes; three second-hand book stalls; a stall selling CDs and a girl selling rides on a porcupine. At the coffee shop, there were old ladies drinking tea; young children stuffing their faces with sticky toffee and Martians tasting the cakes. At the museum, I saw an elephant's skeleton; a stuffed polar bear; a mummified body and a stone carving of what looked like Santa Claus.

P41 PUNCTUATION

Q3
You need these ingredients: olive oil, flour, water, garlic and cheese.
Don't forget these things: tent, sleeping bag, boots, torch, map and compass.
Barbados is wonderful: sun, surf, sea, white sand, cold drinks and coconuts.

Q4
Exercise — it's good for you, honest!
Computers are the future — they're the way forward.;
Visit South America — see Inca ruins, rainforests, and the Andes.

Q5
There were fifty-odd people at the party.
She's my long-lost sister.
He was an old-hand at tennis.
She wore gold-rimmed glasses.

P42 COMMON LETTER STRINGS

Q1

tough — boot
gull — rough
route — look
weight — eight
meat — trough
hook — seat
cough — dull

Q2
foot, watch, bear, one, post; pour, now, move, some, vase

P43 COMMON LETTER STRINGS

Q3
hour — dour, sour; weight — eight, freight; love — dove, shove; pour — four; would — should, could; shave — save, gave, wave, knave

Q4
...any suitable answers.

Q5
bone, moan, tone, own; snow, so, though, beau; boot, flute, suit, route; match, latch, catch, attach
...or any suitable answers.

P44 SPEECH MARKS

Q1
"I'll stay," said Mandy.; Gary yelled, "Look out!"; "I hate shopping," cried Sophie.; The giant growled, "I'm hungry!"

Q2
"I lost a fiver," said Robin. Sheila whispered, "You're late." James replied, "I got lost, Sir." Tracy complained, "It's too hot." "Please explain," said Mr Jones. "I don't believe you," said Boris.

P45 SPEECH MARKS

Q3
Cliff asked, "Why does no one like me?"; "I didn't know that," said Lena.; Sam replied, "Everybody knows that!"; The rats said, "Where's the food?"

Q4
"It's a long shot," said Pete, "but it might just work."; "The murderer," said Shirley Holmes, "was you!"; "There must be a way," she whisperered, "of escaping from this cage."

P46 TYPES OF SENTENCE

Q1
question, statement, question, question, statement

Q2
exclamation, order, question, exclamation, statement

P47 TYPES OF SENTENCE

Q3
Are you happy?; Was it a good day?; Were we late?; Is Elvis hungry?

Q4
Did they do it?; Did you want to go?; Did we come last?; Did she eat the worms?; Did I see her?; Did you feel sick?; Did Andrei bounce a million times on his pogo-stick?

P48 SUFFIXES

Q1

disposable — is fun
unstoppable — can be worn
enjoyable — can be broken
wearable — can't be stopped
breakable — can be thrown away

Q2

edible — can be turned inside out
reversible — can be got into
accessible — can be bent
visible — can be eaten
flexible — can be seen

Q3
possible, reliable, incredible, renewable; flammable, indestructible, sensible, adjustable; movable, unbelievable, available, inflatable

P49 SUFFIXES

Q4
a) intensive, b) talkative, c) impressive, d) massive

Q5
occasion, friction, invasion, vacation, variation, education, location, operation

P50 CONNECTIVES

Q1
a) and, b) or, c) but, d) because, on the other hand

Q2
a) because it didn't fit in the car, b) when the baby took his ice lolly, c) about me in her diary, d) until it was time for tea, e) about giant, green, hairy bugs

P51 CONNECTIVES

Q3
a) however, it is expensive. b) Finally, it gave way altogether. c) you'll never be really good at Maths. d) so they might fall down.

Q4
This will mean that; unfortunately; so; however; The reason for; looking at it another way; If

P52 ITS AND IT'S

Q1
a) its, b) Its, c) its

Q2
a) It's, b) it's, c) It's

Q3
a) its, it's, b) its, It's, c) it's, its, d) It's, It's

P53 COMPOUND WORDS

Q1
a) cupboard, b) starboard, c) handkerchief, d) shepherd, e) necklace, f) breakfast

Q2
a) hopeless, b) useless, c) lifeless, d) Senseless

Q3
Robertson, Robinson; Goldman, Johnson; Guildford, Richardson; Oxford, Bradford

P54 DIMINUTIVES

Q1
towelettes, saplings, seedlings, minibus

Q2
flannelette, owlet, minicab, leaflet, minibus, coverlet

Q3
Danny, Tom/Tommy, Alex, Maggie, Ben, Jo, Lou, Jamie/Jim

P55 ALLITERATION

Q1
a) Betty put a bit of bitter butter in her batter and made her batter bitter. b) It's got a totally terrific tangy taste. c) Summer is the season when we see the sun. d) Philip found Fiona's phone number. e) Wendy wore one wonky wellington and one washed-out sock

Q2
dog, people, stoat, Charley, ball
...or any suitable answers.

Q3
sat, pint, pure, sloppy, plastic

P56 PREFIXES AND SUFFIXES

Q1
un usual ly, mono syllab ic, mathematic al ly, in conclus ive, un economic al, un disiplin ed, anti bio tic, post pone ment, dis tressing ly

Q2
a) vibration, b) translation, c) creation, d) dedication, e) navigation

Q3
competitive; pessimist, unhopeful; Repossession; disproportionate

P57 PREFIXES AND SUFFIXES

Q4
a) tic, b) ful, c) al d) ical, e) ly, f) ation, g) ically

Q5
educational, Victorian, Childhood, information, recorded, Victorian, conditions, social, economic, diabolical, conditions

P58 POSITIVE AND NEGATIVE SENTENCES

Q1
a) ✓, b) ✓, c) ✗, d) ✗

Q2
a) I didn't talk to anyone. b) I don't like watching TV. c) There weren't many people there.

Q3
a) James can swim. b) She liked it. c) Kelly knows who I am. d) I can see the tigers.

Answers are always given column by column, not row by row.